A Man
From
Another World

Don Richardson

Published by EA Books Publishing a division of
Living Parables of Central Florida, Inc. a 501c3
EABooksPublishing.com

Table of Contents

Chapter   Page

1   The Man Descends...1
2   A Symposium Assembles...10
3   A Lesson Commences..15
4   Five More Dubious 'Quick Fixes' 24
5   A Uniquely Different Origin...39
6   Magnetism, Gravity's Co-Star!..50
7   Enhancing Elliptical Galaxies..60
8   Gravity's Unrecognized Complexity 70
9   How Solar Systems Form..85
     Photo section 95
10   The Origin of Matter and Energy...103
11   The Unique Nature of Quarks...116
12   The Ultimate Unrecognized Corollary.......................................125
13   A Unified Field of Truth Unveiled...132
14   And Now, the Seventh Harmony 142
15   Rather Than Avoid Evil, Valcon "Takes It On"!........................153
16   A Geologist Objects to Noah's Flood...165
17   Seven Evocative Pre-Flood Symbols 179
18   Factors That Delay Judgment...184
19   A Crucible Planet's Impending Flashpoint.................................189
20   Fallen Mankind's Grievous History..203

Notes 215

Glossary 216

Chapter One
The Man Descends

John F. Kennedy International Airport flight coordinator Jason Holmes gasped in awe.

"Bill," he whispered hoarsely amid the hubbub in the tower, "please turn around, look up and assure me that what I think I see isn't really there."

Bill Wright, number two on the daytime watch, spun around at his console and shifted his gaze along Jason's upraised arm. Just beyond the tip of Jason's trembling finger, there it was. Bill shuddered. Echoing Jason's gasp, he groaned, "Sorry, Buddy; I'm afraid I see it, too. It's a huge silvery disc. It has just now burst below the clouds and is hovering in mid-air..."

Bill paused, at a loss for words; but Jason continued, shouting now to catch the attention of everyone else in the tower.

"It's as wide as the wingspan of a Boeing 787, with no jets, no windows and no tail fins!" Personnel in other parts of the tower swiveled around and stared up in disbelief.

"Jas," Bill groaned again, "word is that air traffic controllers who see what we are seeing and dare to talk about it lose their jobs. It'll be just our luck if no one else confirms this."

"No fear of that," Jason responded. "Dozens of baggage handlers on the tarmac are gaping up at it, too."

Interrupting their awe, the air-to-tower radio crackled, "Tower, are you there? I request permission to land."

"Who are you?" Jason asked cautiously. "What's your flight number?"

"I have no flight number," a mature voice intoned. "I am Kaidan, a friendly visitor from a distant star system. I am here to liaison with Earth on behalf of a planet called Arkona, but first I need a place to touch down. Nearby air bases are already scrambling military jets to check on me. When they call you, please tell them not to bother. For now, I see a grassy knoll off to the side of your 4R taxiway. If I land there, my vehicle will not impede your regular traffic. Do I have your consent?"

Suddenly breathless, Jason pondered his options. *Do I say "Yes" to seemingly friendly Kaidan from Arkona, only later to be accused of treason for opening the Earth up to an interstellar invasion, or say "No" to Kaidan from Arkona and thus deny mankind what could prove to be the greatest boon the entire cosmos could possibly bestow?*

Staring back at six pairs of eyes that were staring just as fixedly at him, Jason quizzically extended both arms akimbo, palms upward—a mute plea for collegiate advice.

One by one, his colleagues nodded their assent. At last his assistant, Beatrice Johnson, scoffed, "How dare we keep a celestial visitor waiting, Jason? After all, whoever he is, once he sets that big platter down, he'll be Immigration's problem, not ours. Besides, a dozen or more *earthly* flights are about to arrive that are also waiting for our permission to land. What a rare day this has turned out to be!"

Jason nodded and raised the microphone to his lips. His very thumb seemed almost too weighted with destiny to move as required. Steeling his will to press down on the intercom button, Jason instructed the alien pilot nervously: "Roger, Kaidan; we consent! Land your spacecraft carefully at the very center of the location you specified."

"Thank you, Jason, Bill and you others. Don't be concerned. I have come much too far not to land carefully," the voice replied calmly.

Immediately everyone's mind was a-pop with questions:
How could he know our names?
What if he is really an enemy pretending to be friendly?
Does his spaceship emit harmful radiation?
Will JFK services be able to refuel that kind of aircraft?

Moments later, all such queries were shushed as a sober, authoritative voice barked grimly from an overhead speaker: "JFK tower. Wells Air Force Base calling. Do you read me?"

"JFK tower here," Jason replied.

"General Perlman speaking. Our radar shows an unidentified object hovering over JFK. Do you have visual contact with anything like a—a UFO?"

"More than that, General," Jason grinned, "I've been chatting with its pilot. He—or maybe I should say 'It'—very politely requested permission to touch down on a border area of JFK. I granted his request. In fact, he is landing his spaceship at this very moment."

"You granted *what* to *whom?*" Perlman demanded angrily.

"I gave him permission to land, Sir. It seemed a hospitable way to lay out a welcome mat for a visitor all the way from a distant star system."

"Are you joking with me?" Perlman growled.

"Not at all, Sir. I'm speaking what is true. And by the way, our visitor's name is *Kaidan*. He knows you are scrambling jets for an intercept. He said to tell you not to bother. I think you will find him waiting here eager to get acquainted with an authoritative leader like you."

Everyone in the tower burst forth cheering with applause.

Hearing their applause, Perlman (his tone softening) said, "I'm coming to meet—what was his name again?"

"Kaidan, Sir."

Minutes later, the first of several helicopters clattered past the tower heading for Kaidan's landing site on the north side of 4R. World history was embarking on an entirely new phase.

One week later, Dr. Kent Madison, Dean of the School of Religious Studies at Founders University in Virginia, clicked his remote to glean CNN's evening update on the arrival of Kaidan from planet Arkona. As people worldwide already knew by then, Kaidan had refused to emerge from his spaceship until the President of the United States of America, Ronald Forbes, and the United States Congress, plus Gurem Morda and the United Nations General Assembly, jointly granted seven concessions:

1. Kaidan's spaceship must have legal status as planet Arkona's embassy on Earth, preferably on US soil. Also, no attempt may be made by NASA or any other agency to

analyze his spaceship's mechanisms or to dismantle it for purposes of reverse engineering—or even to *enter* it without Kaidan's consent!

2. A spacious forum would be provided for Kaidan to freely share insights from Arkona in a symposium with scientists (especially leaders in the physical sciences—cosmologists, physicists, geologists, *et al.*). Politicians, philosophers and religious leaders could also attend, all at no expense to Kaidan or his home planet.

3. Guests must have multilingual translations as needed.

4. Unabridged video recordings of each lecture/dialogue had to be made available to the public in every nation concerned with no prohibition and at minimal cost.

5. Kaidan agreed to move his 'embassy' to a more suitable location if requested.

6. Kaidan required freedom to leave Planet Earth when he believed his liaison with Earth was well established.

7. Kaidan guaranteed that no harmful microbes would be introduced to Earth's biosphere by his presence on this planet. He would allow medical researchers to x-ray his internal organs and analyze a sample of his blood. Beyond that, he would not be required to submit to any further physical examination.

Kent recalled how eagerly scientists worldwide urged both the United States Congress and the United Nations General Assembly to agree to Kaidan's terms. With both Forbes and Morda adding their consent, all seven conditions Kaidan had specified were speedily ratified by Congress and by the UN. Everyone agreed as well that Arkona's shiny 'embassy' should be relocated away from the noisy perimeter of JFK to a specified area of Central Park. Kaidan consented. Timers avowed that they clocked his craft as completing that move in a mere 55 seconds.

Kent stared in awe as CNN displayed an all-encompassing Plexiglas barrier hastily erected 60 meters from the circular perimeter of Kaidan's cosmic anomaly. On all sides, curious throngs stood staring or clicking cameras in awe while armed guards, posted every 30 degrees around the barrier, provided 24-

hour assurance that no intruder would disturb Kaidan's privacy or violate the security of his only means of return to distant Arkona.

Much discussion had ensued as to a suitable venue for Kaidan's interaction with an international quorum. Madison Square Garden was considered far too large for adequate security. An auditorium at City College of New York was chosen instead as the best local site for Kaidan's interaction with intelligentsia from various nations. Its nearness to Kaidan's 'Embassy in the Park' afforded easy transportation to and from.

Kent gasped to hear a CNN reporter affirm the latest news about Kaidan himself. This alien citizen from far-away Arkona bore the shape of a very trim and healthy human man measuring six foot six inches in height. His skin, however, shimmered as if embedded with particles of pure gold and his blood proved to be a bright shade of aqua. Most surprising of all, an x-ray of Kaidan showed him sporting *two hearts*, organs that take turns beating alternately when at rest or asleep, only to beat in unison for greater efficiency during exercise.

There could be no doubt. Kaidan was not a human masquerading as an alien. He was truly alien yet had somehow become amazingly knowledgeable about the Earth, human culture and the English language.

Settling down with a still-hot microwaved TV dinner at 7 p.m., Kent flicked back and forth from CNN to FOX News Channel. As Kent expected, each network featured a panel of experts selected to mull which aspects of human science, philosophy or even religious belief might soon be verified, improved, rebutted and/or perhaps even totally *replaced* by planet Earth's first-ever, soon-to-be-convened encounter with an interstellar intelligence.

A moment later, Kent gasped again in surprise. He dropped his TV dinner and it landed on the napkin in his lap. He heard CNN announce that the five guests it was hosting for its 7 p.m. program were not only specialists in their respective fields. They were also experts who had learned that very day that they were among the hundreds of persons selected by the International Earth/Arkona Symposium Review Committee to represent Earth's point of view in the forthcoming encounter with Kaidan from Arkona.

Surely this must be the media scoop of the ages, Kent thought, only to find with a click of his remote that five other equally honored guests were being featured on FOX News.

Kent flicked back to CNN, eager to see if he recognized any of the guests. He was disappointed to find that emcee Gregory Moore had already finished the introductions. Kent had to wait.

"Granted, ability to transit multiple light years of interstellar space tags Arkonan technology as far superior to ours," Clyde Smith, dean of the Harvard engineering school, was saying. "But you can be sure NASA and I would, if necessary, gladly donate a kidney and a lung if only Kaidan could show us how to engineer an anti-gravity effect, for example."

"But—as we find again and again here on Earth," philosopher William Stansfield interjected, "our ability to construct superior machines does not guarantee that we will employ those machines benignly. What is it, after all, that our sentient existence in time and space is supposed to demonstrate beyond mere ability to invent new gadgets? Hopefully our friendly star-man Kaidan will offer us some uplifting thoughts about that!"

"In other words," noted atheist Charles Stein volunteered, "does Arkona's spectacular engineering leave the existence of God still unproved?"

Suddenly CNN's camera swung from Stein to a face Kent recognized at once—the face of a man who had been his roommate at the University of Chicago years before. Kent heard his long-ago friend, noted astrophysicist James Engle, respond to Stein, the atheist, with his usual wry grin.

"So a man of your persuasion might hope, Charles. But for someone in my field, the greatest priority will be for Mister, or—should I say—Doctor, Kaidan, to fill in the final details needed to make Big Bang Cosmology's account of cosmic origins complete. As almost everyone in the physical sciences already knows, Big Bang Cosmology stands mathematically and observationally confirmed by the expansion of the cosmos, strong evidence for 'dark matter,' the discovery of 'dark energy' and the background microwave radiation left over from the Big Bang itself. Even so, more details are needed to trace how the cosmos transitioned from that long-ago origin to its present form."

"Surely 'string theory' in physics must also come up for review," offered physicist Homer Grassley, adding: "Besides that, a number of people in my profession would, I think, be as willing as I am to donate a part of my body just to discover what distinguishes one quark from another at the tiniest levels of the sub-atomic world. I'm eager to know if Kaidan may volunteer information about that mystery!"

CNN host Gregory Moore interjected, "On one hand, Panelists, we have church attendance diminishing in the West while radical Islam's increasing jihadist violence—for some people, at least—discredits religion in other ways as well. On the other hand, atheism dominates virtually the entire Communist world and pervades much of Western academia. What if comments by our visitor from Arkona should shatter what remains of the tenuous balance between disbelief and religion in all its various forms? What might then ensue for mankind?"

Later on, Kent paid special attention to a comment by psychiatrist Justine Hobbs, who opined: "Obviously we will all be treading on unexplored ground in this forthcoming symposium. None of us have had the slightest opportunity to study Arkonan psychology ahead of time. What if, for example, someone feels compelled to take issue with Kaidan about something he and Arkonan society happen to honor as *ipso facto* wise and proven?

"For all we know, Kaidan may regard the slightest disagreement from us—mere Earthlings that we are—as an affront. Might he then react by withholding, for example, Arkona's formula for anti-gravity from Clyde's engineering school, just because one of us opposes something his society deems uncontestable?"

At that moment a ping from Kent's nearby laptop announced the arrival of an e-mail from Dr. Matthews, President of Founders University. Kent clicked it open to read:

Dr. Madison, I have just been notified that the International Earth/Arkona Symposium Committee *requests that Founders allow you to serve among a group of theologians representing Christianity at the forthcoming interstellar symposium in NYC. If you accept this privilege, you are expected to arrive at JFK airport for pickup no later than tomorrow evening. Hoping you will accept this invitation on behalf of our faith and Founders University, I offer to release both you and Mrs. Madison from your professorial duties here for at least the next few weeks. Both of you will still be salaried, of course!*

Do you accept?

Kent's mind reeled under the intimidating magnitude of such an enormous responsibility versus the sheer privilege of participating in such an incredible event. There was no doubt. He must accept, whatever the outcome. Kent typed "I accept. Thank you for releasing us!" and hit *Send*.

So! He and former classmate James Engle would now be serving together on the most suspenseful symposium in the entire history of mankind.

Wait! Pondering a moment, Kent asked himself, *Could it be that James exploited his own selection by the committee to recommend me for this?* Years before, Kent recalled, James had actually *chided* Kent for opting to prefer theology over cosmology.

Sinking back in his chair, his mind aglow with awe, Kent gazed across his study. There, set apart in its own separate alcove, his favorite coffee-table tome rested: a five-pound hardcover volume titled *Cosmology Explained*, authored in part by none other than James Engle. Indeed, next to theology, Kent had kept cosmology as his minor. Once again, he recalled how King David's memorable words in Psalm 19 had helped persuade him to choose theology as his major, with cosmology as a hobby he would peruse studiously on the side:

The heavens declare the glory of God; the skies proclaim the work of his hands. Day after day they pour forth speech; night after night they display knowledge. There is no speech or language where their voice is not heard. Their voice goes out into all the earth, their words to the ends of the world.

Deep within, Kent believed that honoring God as Creator must take priority over creation itself. But now a crucial question troubled Kent. Could the ancient psalmist's declaration mean anything to a twin-hearted, hyper-advanced, assumedly ultra-rational stranger from far-away Arkona? Would Kaidan affirm belief in God or would he, like James, disdain faith in anything other than science as secondary if not futile? Might he even regard the notion of a Savior atoning for the sin of the world as ridiculous?

If so, might he himself—theologian Dr. Kent Madison—be obliged to summon the nerve to defend Judeo-Christian tenets by standing firm and perhaps even endeavoring to match wits with an alien? And, if any such response were to offend Kaidan, as Justine Hobbs forewarned might happen, might the alien perhaps react by denying mankind a great leap forward, even withholding Arkonan aid in matters of space engineering? In that event, how could he, Kent Madison, personally endure the blame that would surely ensue on a worldwide scale?

Kent sighed, hoping he and billions of his fellow Earthlings were about to reap a huge harvest in the field of unsolved mysteries as a result of Kaidan's appearance here on Earth. But for the moment, the sound of a door opening and closing distracted him. Turning toward the front door of the condo, Kent called out to his wife and fellow professor.

"Becky, Darling, welcome home from work. You'll never guess where we have to go tomorrow. Do we both have several outfits clean and ready for a quick trip to New York City?"

Chapter Two
A Symposium Assembles

Two mornings later, Kent kissed Becky goodbye in their hotel room and caught a taxi to the campus of the City College of New York. Becky, like many other spouses of Symposium delegates, had to be content to observe proceedings via television in nearby hotel rooms or in their own residences.

After Kent, like every participant, had been scanned and had his ID checked by armed guards at the Forum entrance, Kent pinned a name tag on his lapel and entered CCNY's about-to-be-historic auditorium. Not one but seven large video screens ranged from left to right across a wide stage. Reading his introductory brochure, he learned that each screen was designated for one of the world's seven most-spoken languages. English was designated for the central screen directly behind Kaidan's lectern. Mandarin, Hindustani, Spanish, Russian, Arabic and Portuguese were to appear in simultaneous translation on the six other surfaces.

Kent found his assigned seat in the theological section. Behind him and further back in the same block of seats (a block reserved for religious leaders only), two Roman Catholic cardinals from North and South America, one Jewish rabbi, two Buddhist and two Hindu priests from Asia, plus one Sunni and one Shia Muslim mullah from the Near and Middle East were also present. The latter two, wearing long black and gray beards, had declined to be seated near each other.

Across an aisle to Kent's left, the Symposium's most central block of seats had its foremost rows reserved for people well known in the physical sciences—astronomy, cosmology, geology, physics, chemistry and biology—plus the disciplines of architecture and engineering. Among the 500 appointees selected, they would be the favored few chosen to sit directly in front of

Kaidan when he appeared. Justine Hobbs and Charles Stein, president of the American Atheist Society—due to their participation in CNN's panel—had been invited to join that group.

Kent recalled that Stein, after ten years of marriage to his wife, Alicia, had separated from her a year ago when she became devoutly religious, thereafter refusing to stop praying for him and frequently trying to persuade him about biblical issues. Charles complained he could not bear to "live with someone who foolishly relates every aspect of life to an imaginary God in the sky."

Behind that group, leaders in the social sciences—law, sociology, psychiatry, economics and education—as well as experts in history, archaeology and medicine, occupied the second most favored section. Cultural anthropologists eager to glean insights regarding Arkonan society were also present. Still further back sat UN representatives, politicians, industrialists, military generals, and CIA and FBI agents. Members of the international media were huddled in sound-proofed cubicles so that they could broadcast their comments without disturbing the Symposium as a whole. Event organizers busily conferred with translators and sound technicians in a separate row of cubicles.

Aisle attendants stood ready to offer wireless microphones to any participant wanting to interact publicly with Kaidan.

A moment later James Engle, Kent's long-lost but not forgotten friend from University of Chicago days, caught Kent's eye from across an aisle. Winking at Kent, James tapped a button on his electronic tablet. In the next instant Kent's smartphone vibrated on mute with a text message from James. Kent read:

Good to see you here, K! Good thing your tel # is still the same. Btw, it was I who hyped you to rep Protestant theology here. If God is about to be debunked by our alien visitor, try not to crash in despair. But if your fortitude falters, know I'll be here to hold your hand. On the other hand (pardon the pun), who knows....?

Kent, grinning back across the aisle, texted: *Who knows indeed, bro? But don't worry. If this alien visitor assures us that Jesus reigns as King on the throne of Arkona, I'll be much too exultant to think of gloating! Btw, I saw U & the panel on CNN.*

James texted in return, *all of us on that panel plus Greg Moore, the moderator, have our tablet numbers linked. Any one of us can call everyone during a break or text everyone mid-session with just a press of a button. We call it 'the Loop.' I'll add your # if U want to join us or just monitor our memos. What say U?*

Link me, Kent requested.

Done! James texted.

Moments later a voice was heard over the intercom. "Honored guests, please put every cell phone and electronic device on mute at this time," followed by, "Ladies and gentlemen, allow me to introduce Doctor Grant Adelman, President of City College of New York, and the mayor of New York City, the Honorable Hazel Hines."

Immediately the crowd surged to its feet with eager applause as Adelman and Mayor Hines jointly welcomed the 500 Symposium delegates and also the billions watching or listening via media circuits worldwide. Next, Mayor Hines introduced American President Ronald Forbes and United Nations chief Gurem Morda. Neither Forbes nor Morda was willing to let his vice-president or an aide be the first to shake hands with an interstellar ambassador.

Forbes and Morda expressed their delight that a first-ever encounter with an extra-terrestrial civilization was about to lead to a benign sharing of knowledge.

With that, all four dignitaries turned and extended welcoming arms toward Kaidan as he emerged—tall and lean with a commanding presence—from behind one of the seven screens. Striding forward, beaming a cordial smile, Kaidan shook hands with all four introducers and bid them farewell as they left the premises to return to their official duties.

Locks of silvery hair flowed down to rest on the shoulders of Kaidan's trim-fitting dark green tunic, worn outside black trousers. A golden belt outside his tunic circled his slender waist. Kent noted on his tablet that the golden flecks said to sparkle under Kaidan's skin were not visible from a distance.

At last a beautifully resonant voice that only a few on earth had been privileged to hear up to that moment rang out across the auditorium and, via the media, around the world. Kent imagined billions of speakers of Earth's seven most spoken languages listening and marveling in all 24 time zones of the globe. Yes, at last, Kaidan himself was actually speaking to mankind.

"People of Earth, across 15.36981 light years, now at last the people of my home planet, Arkona, greet you through me, their offered ambassador. Rest assured: *yours is not the only civilization in the vastness of the cosmos.*"

Thunderous applause delayed Kaidan's next statement for almost a minute. Kent observed, however, that Charles Stein's applause was tentative. The avowed atheist was that sort of man who takes pride in being the least impressed observer, no matter what! Kent felt a chill of isolation, wondering if a large majority of the 500 notables invited to the Symposium were just as atheistic as Stein though less outspoken about their unbelief. Even Kent's only friend at the event, Dr. James Engle, was at least agnostic. No matter, the tall alien's next declaration took even Charles Stein by surprise. Kent saw Stein's jaw drop to hear Kaidan say:

"I am pleased to inform you, ladies and gentlemen, that Arkona—my home world—belongs to a consortium of 24 inhabited planets dispersed along this same arm of the Milky Way galaxy that we share with Earth. Thus it is more than just the citizenry of Arkona who greet you via my voice this fine Earth morning. In fact, the citizenry of the 23 other orbs associated with Arkona authorize me to greet you on their behalf as well."

Too stunned even to applaud, the entire audience simply gaped at Kaidan.

"Now, as requested by our Symposium organizers," he continued, "I agree that agenda item number one is for me to compare cosmology and subatomic physics as perceived in the 24-planet Federation with the same two sciences as taught here on Earth. Our primary goal will be to discern an origin consistent with the overall structures of matter in the cosmos. After that we will seek to identify how these most massive structures find their foundation in quarks—those tiny components hidden inextricably inside protons and neutrons.

"Other topics will follow.

"But first, I must fulfill a very personal obligation. I wish to express my deep gratitude to Jason Holmes, Bill Wright, Beatrice Johnson and their fellow staff at the JFK airport control tower for the way they 'kept their cool,' as you say, and even permitted me to land my alien spacecraft on planet Earth. By my special request, three of them are here today on behalf of their entire team. Please, everyone, join me in thanking them before they return to their duties at JFK!"

Jason, Bill and Beatrice stepped forward, aglow with awe to be so honored by Kaidan. Descending from the platform, Kaidan personally shook hands with each honoree amid a standing ovation from the entire Symposium.

Kent's phone buzzed in his pocket. Looking down, he read: *A noble gesture!* The texter was none other than philosopher William Stansfield. Kent and others in the Loop texted agreement.

Beatrice Johnson, speaking into the microphone on Kaidan's lapel, exuded, "Thank you, Kaidan, for privileging us to be your first welcomers. Please help all of us to make this world of ours a nicer place. *We love you!*"

Kaidan's response was a smile that almost seemed to emit a light of its own. As Jason and his group exited the Symposium, Kaidan walked back up onto the platform and turned to address what was now an even more bemused and appreciative audience. Listeners across all 24 time zones waited eagerly to hear his subsequent exposition.

Chapter Three
A Lesson Commences

The mysterious ambassador from Arkona began his formal presentation by saying, "So that everyone will know when I am referring to science as known and applied distinctively here on Earth, I may add the prefix 'terra' (Earth) to the name of that science. Thus I will designate various disciplines as terra-cosmology, terra-physics, terra-astronomy, terra-geology or all of these together as terra-science. I may also distinguish scholars who practice such disciplines on this planet as terra-cosmologists, terra-astronomers, etc.

"Likewise, when I speak of concepts that are familiar to the 24-planet Federation but not known here on Earth, I may then employ 'arko' from the name Arkona as a prefix, thereby easily distinguishing such views as arko-cosmology, arko-physics, or arko-science."

Kent observed hundreds of experts nodding in agreement.

"Surely you scholars—keeping the general public in mind—understand also that I must try," Kaidan added, "to present science in language that is not overly technical."

Dozens of experts nodded again, some chuckling over how hard it could be to help the public grasp certain sciences. As for Kent in the Symposium and Becky watching by a hotel-room television, they had prayed earnestly that morning for divine help to understand whatever Kaidan might say. They also knew, however, that close attention on their own part was essential.

"Because a majority of people viewing this Symposium worldwide," Kaidan opined, "are barely aware of the latest in cosmology as developed on Earth, let me first recount two valid discoveries terra-specialists have made recently. After that, I will critique certain speculations which they believe ensue from those two valid realizations."

Oh, the suspense! James Engle thought to himself. *Are we, earthbound thinkers and authors of university textbooks, about to be vindicated for valid insights or chided for faulty conclusions?*

Kent, from a theological perspective, was praying fervently, knowing that classes in thousands of schools, colleges and universities worldwide were amended to permit half a billion bright teens, undergrads, graduate students, teachers and professors to be exposed to whatever views Kaidan was about to confer. Also, via live television and radio broadcasts, the entire Symposium was being streamed live on the Internet. College professors were available to explain scientific terms at special gatherings as needed. Even wardens of certain State and Federal prisons were allowing tens of thousands of inmates to listen to Kaidan via television.

Could arko-wisdom charm terra-criminals to live lawfully?

God, Kent implored, *if it happens that this alien named Kaidan does not believe in you as Creator of the heavens and the earth, please overrule the consequences! Since virtually all of mankind is listening, may this alien visitor wield his influence for good and not for ill! And please help me understand what he says.*

Kaidan, meanwhile, posted a topic on all seven screens:

TWO FACTS MOST COSMOLOGISTS ACCEPT

"To begin!" Kaidan resumed, striding out from behind his lectern. "While terra-physicists were powering up ever-larger particle accelerators to study things as tiny as quarks, terra-astronomers were using increasingly far-sighted telescopes to examine the cosmos at large. Gazing ever deeper into space, of course they detected, photographed and began studying and classifying stars, nebulae and enormous numbers of galaxies in various shapes and sizes.

"Soon, two facts became clear to most terra-scientists," Kaidan segued. "Fact One: the majority of galaxies are receding away from each other and from Earth ever more rapidly. Fact Two: experts find further that this ongoing dispersion of galaxies is due not only to their individual motions but also to an actual ballooning of the space-time continuum in which they exist. The cause of that massive ballooning of the space-time continuum is a force terra-scientists call 'dark energy.'

"'Dark *energy*'—a confirmed phenomenon—must not be confused, however, with terra-science's hypothetical 'dark matter,' a moot subject I'll say more about later. For now, let's move on to the next consideration.

OPPOSITE SPECULATIONS ABOUT THOSE FACTS

"To explain why the cosmos is expanding," Kaidan continued, "terra-theorists pondered two options. In 'Option A,' the confirmed *expansion* of the cosmos is viewed as *corollary* to, or ensuing from, an earlier era when the cosmos was *contracting*. Some terra-theorists even posited a *pulsating* cosmos in which everything collapses in a so-called 'Big Crunch' only to explode again with an ensuing 'Big Bang.' Some viewed these two events as recycling each other, perhaps endlessly.

"Finding this concept unprovable, most scholars dismissed Option A in favor of something I call 'Option B'—a 'Big Bang' prior to which the cosmos simply did not exist and after which it simply continues expanding." Kaidan posted his next topic.

AN OVERLOOKED VARIATION OF 'OPTION A'

"Arko-cosmology favors an alternate version of Option A. I call it the 'Cinderella's Slipper Version' because it describes the origin of the cosmos in a way that 'fits the foot' of everything we see around us. How sad! Terra-thinkers missed a golden opportunity to describe the present expansion of the cosmos as corollary to an earlier era in which the cosmos was indeed born *contracting inwardly* from an external source rather than exploding from a tiny point. But this contraction—because it was accompanied by *axial spin*—did not end in a 'Big Crunch' at all. Rather, conserved angular momentum triggered such intense centrifugal force that all the individual stars, globular clusters and galaxies that coalesced readily during the contraction phase were hurled back out and are still being hurled back out toward that same still far-away exterior plane of origin.

"Just as an ice skater spinning slowly with her arms outstretched *spins faster* when she draws her arms in, so also—once hosts of stars, globular clusters and galaxies had formed—intense centrifugal force hurled everything back out, overruling the potential for a 'Big Crunch.'

"Everything else from protons to planets to stars to galaxies spins! Why not posit the cosmos as equipped with a corollary axial spin as well?

"Permit me to 'spin' a major perk of this alternate version of Option A, the 'Cinderella's Slipper Option.' Prior to the time when intensified centrifugal force redirected a contracting cosmos outbound, 'dark energy,' originally contracting with a contracting cosmos and thus abetting the coalition of stars, globular clusters and galaxies, also underwent a change of direction. Slowing gradually as it approached an apex of contraction, dark energy switched over to begin its present accelerating *expansion* phase! As a result, hosts of individual stars, globular clusters and galaxies began to be pushed ever faster out at even more acute angles toward their present-day positions.

"Even Isaac Newton, three centuries ago, posited a finite but originally dispersed cosmos contracting gravitationally but, alas, *with no spin and no reversible 'dark energy.'* In a 1692 letter to Richard Bentley, master of Trinity College at Cambridge University, Newton wrote:

"'If all the matter in the universe were evenly scattered throughout all the heavens, and every particle had an innate gravity toward all the rest...the matter on the outside of the space would, by its gravity, tend toward all the matter on the inside, and by consequence, fall down into the middle of the whole space and there compose one great spherical mass.'[1]

"Newton saw contraction as reducing everything to 'one great spherical mass.' If only he had added a factor of conserved angular momentum to his prescient notion of cosmic contraction, he would have positioned himself even further ahead of his time."

Cosmologists Earth-wide were listening to Kaidan in awe. As best James could recall, none of his fellow cosmologists who posited the cosmos as pulsating with successive 'Big Crunches' and ensuing 'Big Bangs' had thought to factor Kaidan's spin-induced angular momentum and reversible dark energy into their theory. And who could imagine an alien from a far-away world quoting something Isaac Newton wrote in 1692?

What an intriguing option! James reasoned. A cosmic contraction combined with conserved angular momentum and dark energy reversing at an apex could indeed replace a 'Big Crunch' with a 'Fling It All Back Out' model. And that model could indeed solve many problems bedeviling Big Bang Cosmology itself.

James recalled that Dr. Michael Longo at the University of Michigan had indeed found some evidence for a spinning cosmos. Yet even he and his team of graduate students had offered their version of cosmic spin as ensuing *from* a 'Big Bang,' rather than *entirely replacing all need for* such an event. Kaidan posted:

CRITIQUING 'OPTION B'S' BIG BANG

"I am eager to show you many remarkable facets of Option A's initially-contracting-later-expanding cosmology," Kaidan assured everyone. "But first let me try to help uninitiated listeners and viewers fathom why a majority of terra-scientists believe they have achieved success with a very *opposite* approach to the puzzle of cosmic origins, namely, Option B's Big Bang!

"Big Bang proponents claim that the present expansion of the cosmos and a few other factors require us to believe that the more than 100 billion galaxies that fill this cosmos all emanated from a 'Big Bang,' an explosive event that occurred at a tiny point billions of years ago."

Kent saw James and his fellow cosmologists in the Symposium lean back deeper in their chairs, readying themselves for a critical review of their favorite theory—Big Bang Cosmology [BBC]. Their eyes darted nervously from Kaidan to the seven screens featuring his texts and illustrations. It would not be easy for noted scholars if their supposedly well-established conclusions based on well-funded research were about to be refuted by an alien intellect. Kent prayed that if indeed that conclusion were unavoidable, Kaidan would sensitively try to spare terra-scientists at least some measure of embarrassment.

WHAT WAS BBC'S MAIN EVENT—REALLY?

"Scholars favoring BBC—a huge majority—ought to tell the public why their 'Big Bang' had to be so BIG," Kaidan continued. "Most people assume the origin of the 100 billion or so galaxies we see around us was BBC's 'main event.' They don't know that these same scholars actually regard the 100 billion galaxies of our universe as just a *tiny residue* left over from something *enormously* bigger. Their theory requires a *billion* times more matter than is in this entire cosmos to appear at a tiny point all intermixed with an equal amount of antimatter only then to explode, leaving these 100 billion galaxies as a tiny residue!"

He's right, James thought with a twinge of conscience. He and other Big Bang popularizers were indeed prone to fudge their theory's major prerequisite. According to Big Bang theory, this entire cosmos is only "a tiny residue" left after the otherwise total annihilation of mass equal to two billion universes in which matter and antimatter were evenly intermixed hence sure to explode. After all, why strain public credulity with a mind-numbing prerequisite when its aftermath alone was stymying enough?

"If matter and antimatter are intermixed," Kaidan added, "they convert each other *totally* from mass to energy via Einstein's famous equation, $E=mc^2$. As terra-scientists are all well aware, if anything of either component remained, two laws of physics, conservation of mass and conservation of *charge*, are violated! In other words, *all* of the matter and *all* of the antimatter should have fled the scene as energy after the Big Bang. What then are we to conclude, hearing Big Bang theorists tell us that *all* the antimatter converted to energy and fled the scene of the Big Bang but matter enough for these 100 billion galaxies remained intact?

"Either we must conclude that the cosmos permits two valid laws of physics—conservation of mass and conservation of charge—to be violated or else Big Bang Cosmology is *wrong*. To avoid the onerous choice, BBC theorists had to invent a new physical law as follows.

"To save the day for BBC, terra-physicists had to claim that when extremely enormous, awesomely large quantities of both matter and antimatter intermix, nature actually does favor matter over antimatter by sparing *one part of matter* for every one billion parts of matter that co-annihilate with one billion parts of antimatter. They claim to have proof that 'charge parity asymmetry' prevails to that extent over two longstanding conservation laws of physics. Let me cite an example of that claim.

"Astrophysicist Neil de Grasse Tyson and co-author Donald Goldsmith, in the 2004 edition of their tome titled *Origins: Fourteen Billion Years of Cosmic Evolution*, describe how 'charge parity asymmetry' purportedly works. Note how these two learned men declare that:

"For reasons unknown, [the] symmetry between matter and antimatter had been 'broken' at the [precise moment of the Big Bang], which led to a slight excess of matter over antimatter. The asymmetry was small but crucial for the future evolution of the universe: for every 1 billion antimatter particles, **1 billion + 1 matter particles** were born .... [Emphasis added].[2]

"Tyson and Goldsmith, straining for a semblance of plausibility, speak only of 1 billion 'particles' of this and 1 billion 'particles' of that sparing one 'particle' of matter. They know most readers will not compute what they actually mean, namely that Big Bang Cosmology requires one billion **universes** of particles of matter to co-annihilate with one billion **universes** of particles of antimatter to spare all the particles of matter needed to comprise the one matter-only universe. Not only so, but all of these two billion universes of mass must co-annihilate at a tiny point so that our one matter-only universe can exist at all. Are we really too naïve to do the math? Yes, Neil and Donald, your 'asymmetry was small' indeed but the mass that had to be involved was HUGE.

"These noted authors continue:

"Had this matter over antimatter asymmetry not emerged, the expanding universe would forever be composed of light and nothing else.[3]

"Then again, a few pages later, the same authors assert:

"Every billion annihilations left...only a single **hadron**... mute testimony to the tiny excess of matter over antimatter in the early universe....Without the imbalance of a billion and one to a mere billion between matter and antimatter *particles*, all the mass in the universe (except for the dark matter whose form remains unknown) would have annihilated before the universe's first second had passed [emphasis added].[4]

"There you go again, Doctors Tyson and Goldsmith," Kaidan said, imitating Ronald Reagan's presidential debate rejoinder decades earlier. "You say 'particles' when '2 billion *universes of particles*' is what you really mean. Note how Tyson and Goldsmith aver that for every billion annihilations, just one *'hadron'* was conserved. What *is* a hadron?

"Hadrons are sub-atomic particles with at least a little more mass than electrons and positrons. A positron is the antimatter equivalent of an electron. Small hadrons, such as kaons and pions, unlike their much larger cousins—protons and neutrons—are extremely unstable. An average pion, for example, decays after only 2.6 times 10 to the minus-eight [2.6×10^{-8}] seconds.

"As for pions and kaons, they contribute *absolutely no mass* to the formation of atoms, molecules, elements, stars and worlds! Protons and neutrons (and electrons for that matter) are believed stable enough to match *the age of the cosmos*! All this to note that the only 'hadrons' *thought* to favor matter over antimatter by that billion-to-one margin are extremely short-lived ones!

"How accurate can a two-billion-to-one measurement be on particles that last millionths of a second? Meanwhile, 'charge parity asymmetry' has never been claimed for protons, neutrons and electrons, the primary building blocks of matter.

"For two authors to name-drop 'hadrons,' hinting that even *stable* hadrons—protons and neutrons—also confirm 'charge parity asymmetry,' when the opposite is true, is *very* ill-advised.

"On this topic, let me attest to people everywhere on planet Earth that terra-science's 'charge parity asymmetry' is totally unknown everywhere else on 24 other inhabited planets of the Interstellar Federation!

"One would think Big Bang theorists, rather than posit such an easy 'quick fix' based entirely on 'reasons unknown,' would first question whether their starting supposition of a Big Bang was valid at all. Asking that question could have led them to reexamine Option 'A,' a much more promising approach to the origin of the cosmos. Alas, they chose not to seek an alternative. At least here now follows Big Bang Cosmology's leading quick fix."

With another click of his hand-held remote, Kaidan posted a statement on all seven screens arrayed behind him. The statement summarized what he had just explained about Big Bang Cosmology's dependence on conservation of both mass and charge being violated so that enough matter for this universe would survive the Big Bang. The statement declared:

BBC'S QUICK FIX # 1: IMPLY THAT 'CHARGE PARITY ASYMMETRY' IS MANIFEST EVEN AMONG PROTONS AND NEUTRONS, WHERE IN FACT IT IS UNKNOWN

Kent winced with sympathy for James and the entire natural sciences community. Kent knew that Engle's own writings concurred heavily with Tyson and Goldsmith's cosmology. Kaidan was by no means mincing words.

"Before I explain what terra-theorists could have found had they simply reexamined Option A," Kaidan added, "let me present five more quick fixes theorists construe to prop up BBC."

Chapter Four
Five More Dubious 'Quick Fixes'

"I now draw your attention to a further flaw by authors Tyson and Goldsmith in the tome I cited earlier," Kaidan stated.

"A star with a mass greater than about a hundred times the Sun's will have a luminosity so great—such an enormous outpouring of energy in the form of visible light, infrared, and ultraviolet—that any additional gas and dust attracted toward the star, will be pushed away by the intense pressure of starlight....This radiation pressure operates so effectively that just a few high-mass stars within a dark, obscuring cloud will have luminosities sufficient to disperse nearly all its interstellar matter.[5]

"Yet both authors also describe elsewhere in their book an even greater radiation pressure with the following description:

"If...a single anti-star were to annihilate with a single ordinary star, the conversion of their matter and antimatter into gamma-ray energy would be swift, violent and total.[6]

"When Tyson and Goldsmith," Kaidan said with a twinkle, "describe the mass of one star and one anti-star converting each other *totally* to radiation, they unwittingly annul a major premise of Big Bang Cosmology. BBC needs a cosmic 'bias' to guarantee that *one-billionth* of the matter in any such co-annihilation will survive as matter! Scholars, make up your minds; is your co-annihilation partial or total? Tyson and Goldsmith also claim that:

"...their melding would produce an object so luminous that it would temporarily out-produce all the energy of all the stars of 100 million galaxies and fry us to an untimely end. We have no compelling evidence that such an event has ever occurred anywhere in the universe.[7]

"First we are told that for this present universe to exist at all, one billion universes of matter had to 'meld' with one billion universes of anti-matter. Now, both authors assure us that not even matter and antimatter equal to the mass of *just two* stars has ever melded! Which of these opposite claims should we believe?

"Tyson and Goldsmith express awe at how much *pressure* the gamma radiation released by the melding of *just one* star with *just one* anti-star would exert on the cosmos. Yet both authors overlook how much expulsive pressure the radiation released by their posited 'melding' of one billion universes of mass together with one billion universes of anti-mass would have exerted on that mere one-billionth of the matter that supposedly survived.

"Surely everyone must realize—if a Big Bang actually happened—a mega-tsunami of gamma radiation would have summarily blasted every particle of that relatively minuscule bit of matter, probably almost at light-speed, far, far beyond the outermost perimeter of what is now the entire cosmos. How could even one proton have remained to participate in star formation? *Charge parity asymmetry notwithstanding, the cosmos would not exist at all!*"

Kent and William Stansfield—both familiar with James Engle's books and articles on cosmology—saw James grimace with embarrassment. As he and they all knew, nowhere in his writings had he ever mentioned the Big Bang as creating a horrendous radiation pressure problem for Big Bang Cosmology's relatively tiny residue of surviving matter.

As if reading their minds, Kaidan commented, "Many other authors are just like Tyson and Goldsmith—articulate about radiation pressure exerted by lesser events yet mute about the gamma radiation pressure that their posited melding of two billion universes of mass and anti-mass would have exerted on the relative iota of matter that purportedly remained. So! Let me now present Big Bang Cosmology's quick fix #2 on all seven screens.

BBC'S QUICK FIX # 2: IGNORE THE RADIATION PRESSURE THAT WOULD HAVE ENSUED IF TWO BILLION UNIVERSES HAD ACTUALLY CONVERTED FROM MASS TO RADIATION IN A BIG BANG

"Ignoring the radiation pressure factor is only number two in a series of quick fixes terra-scholars have had to improvise just to keep Big Bang Cosmology masquerading as tenable. A third quick fix was needed to offset two other problems.

"Problem A: With mass equal to one billion universes plus one billion anti-universes concentrated at the site of the Big Bang, wouldn't *gravity* have been intense enough at that tiny point to completely negate any and every possibility of expansion? And:

"Problem B: Temperature indicators show that the entire cosmos manifests the same average temperature everywhere. Wouldn't a Big Bang's incredible release of energy leave the actual site where it happened considerably hotter than the rest of the cosmos? Why did that not happen?

"Some terra-cosmologists almost deserted BBC due to these two questions. Others said, 'Maybe matter had to undergo a phase transition before gravity could appear,' begging the question, 'how can matter without gravity still be called matter?'"

Clyde Smith texted the Loop with, *Seems he doesn't know that astrophysicist Alan Guth solved that problem for BBC back in 1979*, only to hear Kaidan say, a moment later:

"Then, in 1979, a scientist named Alan Guth revived hope by offering Big Bang cosmologists a novel 'solution.'" (Kaidan used his fingers to simulate quote marks in the air.) "I call it—"

Again, Kaidan clicked a third big notice on-screen. It read:

BBC'S QUICK FIX # 3: AN "INFLATIONARY EPOCH"

"Guth theorized that the space-time continuum itself— which I will hereafter simply call the 'extent' continuum—at the precise instant of the posited Big Bang, ballooned outward in all directions several thousand times faster than the speed of light! Thus two billion universes of mass not only escaped gravity's confining clutch but also got the heat of their melding evenly distributed everywhere! The sudden rapid dispersal of mass rendered gravity too weak to prevent the Big Bang. Plus, any excess heat that might have betrayed where the Big Bang actually happened became spread so evenly that every theorist had an excuse for not knowing where the posited big event happened.

"For Big Bang cosmologists to disregard conservation of both charge and mass and then enthrone 'charge parity asymmetry' in its place was not their only oddity. Needing to cheat gravity and thin out the heat of the Big Bang," Kaidan mock-marveled, "they also assign virtual omnipotence to the extent continuum by enabling it to convey, in a fraction of a second, two billion universes of mass or its equivalent in terms of radiation—not in one direction, mind you, but in *all* directions. And that, of course, had to happen thousands of times faster than the speed of light."

By that time Clyde Smith was slumping down in his seat, wishing he had stifled his most recent text. Kaidan continued:

"But wait! Accelerating mass equal to two billion galaxies thousands of times faster than the speed of light would invest that huge mass with an unimaginable amount of momentum, wouldn't it? So what could possibly slow that much mass back down to relatively pedestrian cosmic rates? Guth simply assumed that everything slowed as suddenly and as easily as it accelerated.

"Anything that solves a problem for Big Bang theory has to be possible, no matter how fanciful.

"And that, Friends, is how we find Big Bang Cosmology's quick fix number one—charge parity violation—complemented by quick fix number two, i.e., simply ignore the pressure that radiation would have exerted on the relative iota of surviving matter. And all of this is complicated further by quick fix number three—Big Bang Cosmology's need for an 'inflationary epoch' (as if an event that lasted a mere millionth of a second could be called an 'epoch'!)."

James felt his face blushing with embarrassment. To his knowledge no one had ever critiqued Big Bang Cosmology with even a fraction of the devastating logic Kaidan was applying so flawlessly before the very eyes and ears of the entire planet. The challenge of finding an alternate theory had stymied everyone.

"Brace yourselves," Kaidan continued. "This is only the beginning. BBC's quick-fix numbers four, five and six have yet to try to lull us into an ever deeper state of gullibility!"

James texted everyone on the Loop: *BBC proponents everywhere are wiping sweat from their brows, and this ordeal is maybe only half over! Bad enough to eat humble pie just in this forum, but this is going worldwide?!!*

Charles Stein texted back: *Wait till K tries to explain Arkona's 'Cinderella' version, bro. Find flaws in it, and the score will be Earth 1, Arkona 1, in this intellectual war of two worlds.*

That response made Kent, James, Justine and others on the Loop wince, except perhaps for CNN host Greg Moore, who was focused on even higher ratings for the next panel discussion on CNN. Might it perhaps draw 100 million viewers?

Homer Grassley texted, *I'm struck by the realization that Kaidan is affirming doubts I myself have had about BBC but was too cowed to moo about. I say, Let's man-up and let what actually makes sense and doesn't violate known laws prevail!*

Kaidan, meanwhile, had posted a fourth 'Quick Fix' under his three initial headings. Appropriate translations on various screens introduced the next topic.

BBC'S QUICK FIX # 4: DARK MATTER

Seeing abashed expressions on the faces of scientists seated in the first few rows, Kaidan continued. "On page 149 of the same source I cited earlier, Tyson and Goldsmith admit that even long after the posited Big Bang, many gas clouds in galaxies were prone not to form stars at all, due mainly to 'turbulent motion' within the gas, magnetic interference and other factors. Both authors even make this striking admission:

"... we must allow for the fact that the universe has been expanding ever since the big bang, naturally opposing any tendency for matter to clump together by gravity. The problem...becomes more serious when we consider that the cosmos expanded most rapidly soon after the big bang.... [Probably a reference to Alan Guth's posited post-big bang 'inflation.'] ...At first glance, we could no more rely on gravity to form massive objects out of diffuse gas than we could use a shovel to move fleas across a barnyard. Yet somehow gravity has done the trick.[8]

"Then only one chapter later," Kaidan stated, "these same two authors assert the following:

"The scary part of this...[is] that if no one knew in advance that stars exist, front-line research would offer plenty of convincing reasons why stars could never form.[9]

"Both authors, speaking of 'scary' forces that obviously would have hindered gravity from coalescing stars, make no mention of the enormously scarier radiation pressure that Big Bang-generated gamma rays would have exerted on that relatively tiny iota of expanding matter had there been a Big Bang. How could they possibly overlook so major a factor?

"With gravity due to Big Bang-generated ordinary matter totally unable to coalesce stars, terra-cosmologists began conjuring up another kind of mass called 'dark matter,' a substance which had to be quantitative enough to wield gravity six times stronger than ordinary matter. Question: did this dark matter also originate in the Big Bang or did it predate the cosmos? Strangely, terra-cosmologists avoid crediting the Big Bang as sourcing dark matter. Note how Doctors Tyson and Goldsmith insist that terra-science needs 'dark matter' without saying anything about its origin! Shouldn't they credit the Big Bang as making room for it as well?

"...the universe responds to two competing effects: gravity wants to make stuff coagulate, but the expansion [of the cosmos] wants to dilute it. If you do the math, you rapidly deduce that the gravity from ordinary matter could not win this battle by itself. It needed the help of dark matter, without which we would be...in a universe with...no galaxies, no stars, no planets, no people. How much gravity from dark matter did it need? Six times as much as that provided by ordinary matter itself....try as you may, you cannot credit ordinary matter [alone].[10]

"Now think with me about the implications. First, terra-cosmologists tell us that a mere residue of the original mass of matter is all that was still recognizable as matter after the Big Bang. Everything else, they claim, fled the scene as photons of energy. Now the same theorists, changing their minds, imply but do not say that *at least six times as much of something else called 'dark matter' also survived the Big Bang!*

"Big Bang Cosmology collapses unless at least six times as much 'dark matter' survived the Big Bang along with ordinary matter. This, of course, adds that much more mass for the extent continuum to have to accelerate far beyond the speed of light and then brake back down to a snail's pace.

"Dark matter is so named because despite how much of it supposedly exists, it remains invisible to telescopes. In other words, dark matter remains 'dark' because it cannot absorb and then re-emit photons of energy.

"But that is only the beginning of dark matter's 'darkness.' Inasmuch as ordinary matter had to appear with antimatter and then instantly meld with antimatter after the Big Bang, why don't BBC theorists suggest that dark matter also had to co-appear with *anti-dark matter* and then meld with the same?

"They have to be mum about that for obvious reasons.

"Melding, you see, requires a release of energy as per $E=mc^2$; but emitting radiation would render dark matter detectable, which dark matter cannot be! Also, the pressure of energy released by dark matter melding with anti-dark matter would prevent dark matter gravity from coalescing ordinary matter as stars. So let's not hold our breath awaiting comments about dark matter having anti-dark matter as a corollary. Earth's entire astrophysical community remains conspiratorially mum about any possibility or need for *anti*-dark matter.

"Ordinary matter's ability to absorb photons," Kaidan continued, "often triggers something called *ionization* in ordinary matter. For the benefit of listeners unfamiliar with the term 'ionization,' here is what it means: Any atom in which protons in the nucleus outnumber electrons orbiting the nucleus is said to be ionized. Photons often act like busybodies that knock electrons out of orbit, thus changing normal atoms into ions which in turn generate magnetic fields in the surrounding space.

"So, if dark matter consists of 'dark atoms' with something akin to dark electrons orbiting around dark protons, dark matter's inability to absorb photons of energy preempts dark matter from becoming ionized! Apart from ionization, neither can dark matter be encompassed by magnetic fields! Therefore, dark matter will be invisible not only to telescopes but to magnetometers as well!

"Thus gravity, according to terra-theorists, is the only force dark matter is able to wield. How odd that anything called 'matter' could be so strangely limited. Yet even gravity is oddly limited in the context of dark matter. Here is why.

HOW ODD! DARK MATTER GRAVITY COALESCES ORDINARY MATTER BUT NOT DARK MATTER ITSELF

"Gravity consistently causes everything in a given quantity of ordinary matter to coalesce *radially toward a center of mass* in ordinary matter. Though dark matter gravity supposedly pulls ordinary matter radially toward centers of dark matter mass, that same dark matter mass never accounts for any part of that coalesced mass after it has been coalesced! So dark matter somehow manages to vacate the scene once its attracting work is done. In other words, dark matter is immune to its own gravity and even to ordinary matter's gravity as well.

"If indeed 60 percent or so of the cosmos consists of gravitationally active dark matter, surely massive amounts of dark matter should be found wearing a skin of ordinary matter like an orange wears a rind. Indeed the inner 60 percent of every star and galaxy should consist of nothing but dark matter.

"Undeterred by logical objections, Big Bang cosmologists steadfastly credit dark matter as pulling galaxies together initially, only later to exit so as to remain thinly dispersed *around* the same galaxies they coalesced. Wouldn't any ordinary matter that followed dark matter in to form galaxies in the first place also follow dark matter back *out* when it left?

"Why do theorists posit dark matter as coalescing galaxies and then exiting to their exteriors to 'hang out'? There is only one response. If 'dark matter' does not encompass galaxies, terra-science has no way to explain why certain stars far from the center of galaxies are moving unexpectedly fast.

"In the larger cosmos, terra-cosmologists also claim that invisible dark matter has to be present to explain why galaxies in large galactic clusters are moving more rapidly than can be explained by just the ordinary matter in the clusters themselves.

"Both phenomena—the rapid motion of stars in the exterior of galactic arms and the rapid motion of galaxies in galactic clusters—are subjects I will explain later.

"Tyson and Goldsmith are not alone in attesting the need for dark matter despite poor evidence for its existence. In a tome about cosmology, author Giles Sparrow argues that dark matter gravity, to be credible, has to be able to coalesce matter despite horrendous radiation pressure to the contrary. Sparrow wrote:

"But if radiation was forcing normal matter apart up until this time [i.e., until some 300,000 years after the Big Bang], how could structure begin to form? *The only answer is that the CMBR's ripples* [i.e., ripples in the Cosmic Microwave Background Radiation] *are echoes of dark matter in the early universe*. Particles of such matter *would be unaffected* (or at least *minimally affected*) by the torrents of radiation around them and could have begun their slow gravitational collapse early, forming 'seeds' of material [dark matter] around which visible matter—the matter of stars, planets and galaxies, could later condense [emphasis added].[11]

"Friends, if 'stars, planets and galaxies' coalesced *around* 'seeds of dark matter,' surely those 'seeds of dark matter' should still be present in the cores of billions of stars, planets and galaxies today. How strange! Neither astrophysicists nor geologists ever mention the slightest presence of 'dark matter' when analyzing the actual composition of stars and planets. And why do astrophysicists always speak of dark matter as something that is forever *external* to galaxies rather than imbedded in their cores?

"Also keep in mind, please, that the instantaneous hyper-inflation of the entire baby cosmos posited by Alan Guth—if it really happened—barred both dark matter gravity and ordinary matter gravity from coalescing matter while it was still relatively concentrated despite its explosive expansion.

"Post-inflation, with low-mass elements like hydrogen and helium still expanding rapidly due to intense gamma radiation pressure, how could stars—let alone galaxies—form at all?

"Frankly," Kaidan advised, "BBC's description of how not only stars but also galaxies formed is totally untenable.

"As I will soon show, positing the cosmos as having undergone Option A's earlier era of a single dark energy contraction will account for all of the contingencies that Tyson, Goldsmith and Sparrow rely on dark matter to explain.

"Something else touted as forensic proof for a Big Bang," Kaidan advised, "is the 1964 discovery of a steady flow of microwave radiation, dubbed by Sparrow in the quote above as 'cosmic microwave background radiation' or CMBR. Most scholars, however, abbreviate CMBR to CBR—i.e., cosmic background radiation. CBR is so named because it is streaming toward us omni-directionally; i.e., it approaches everywhere in the middle cosmos from everywhere in the distant cosmos. This leads me to focus attention on BBC's *fifth* major attempt at self-rescue.

BBC'S QUICK FIX # 5: CBR MISINTERPRETED!

"Inasmuch as CBR arrives omni-directionally, where must its source or sources be located? One could guess that CBR's source, even if not seen, cannot be confined to one small region of space. Photons fly straight unless *refracted* while passing through transparent substances like air or water, so the source of radiation arriving omni-directionally via non-refracting empty space must be a source that encompasses the entire cosmos! That is precisely the kind of all-encompassing exterior source that Arkona's Option A-based cosmology provides for the CBR.

"Yet Big Bang cosmologists have to posit CBR, despite its startling omni-directionality, as sourced at just *one* location far out in space and far back in time—the site of the Big Bang. Nor do they explain why a single enormous burst of radiation emitted billions of years ago and traveling outbound at the speed of light— 300,000 kilometers per second!—did not leave 100 billion relatively slow-moving galaxies *far behind ages ago, assuming that much radiation would have allowed galaxies to form at all!*

"Some scholars try to account for CBR's photons deviating from straight line flight by claiming that space itself is so curved that whatever goes out must also come back around. Yet Tyson and Goldsmith shun that recourse. On page 95 of their book they agree with other cosmologists that the extent continuum is *flat*.

"Still, everyone fails to explain why radially dispersed CBR 'dilly-dallies' within the visible universe at all, instead of leaving everything far behind eons ago. Perhaps those speedy CBR photons looked back and said, 'The galaxies aren't matching our pace, so let's slow down and turn back. Ages from now people in those galaxies will need to be able to see us as forensic evidence for Big Bang Cosmology.

"And this brings us to..." Again one click of Kaidan's remote added a sixth message under the previous five.

BBC'S QUICK FIX # 6: APPEAL TO UV RADIATION TO SOLVE ITS INTRINSIC 'DARK ERA' PROBLEM

"Here's what Big Bang cosmologists believe," Kaidan advised. "After their two billion universes of matter and antimatter had melded, all the protons and electrons spared by so-called 'charge parity asymmetry' were left thoroughly intermixed and available to each other in unavoidably equal numbers. So all those protons and electrons began doing exactly what protons and electrons are expected to do: they united to form *atomic* hydrogen!

"That was problematic. You see, protons *without* electrons were exactly the kind of hydrogen needed for the cosmos—*the ionized kind.* Having equal numbers of protons and electrons in the aftermath of the Big Bang assured that neutral atomic hydrogen would be the exclusive raw material available to make stars. Let me explain why ionized hydrogen would have been a *boon* for the infant cosmos whereas atomic hydrogen could only be a *bane*.

"(A). *Ionized* hydrogen and helium are always attended by magnetism in addition to gravity. The absence of ionized hydrogen and helium in the aftermath of the Big Bang excludes magnetism from being there to help gravity amass stars. Otherwise magnetism would have amassed matter at its poles as a prelude to gravity drawing matter toward consequent centers of mass to form stars.

"(B). Ionized hydrogen and helium's lack of electrons also renders both gases relatively *transparent*. Atomic hydrogen and helium, where protons and electrons are balanced, become relatively opaque as a result. Today's stars shine freely because their hydrogen and helium are 90 percent ionized and only 10 percent atomic. Post-Big Bang stars—made solely of opaque atomic gases and embedded in clouds of the same—could barely shine. What light they emitted was blocked by clouds of opaque gas that had not yet coalesced as stars, hence BBC's 'dark era'!

"According to Big Bang theory, what enabled BBC's infant cosmos to change massive amounts of the *wrong* kind of hydrogen into the kind that prevails in today's cosmos, i.e., hydrogen that is 90 percent ionized? How did their cosmos segue from a 'dark era' due to exclusively *atomic* hydrogen to a 'brighter' era wherein hydrogen is predominantly *ionized*?

WHY BBC FAILS TO CURE ITS 'DARK ERA' PROBLEM

"To explain how a Big Bang-generated cosmos transitioned from its built-in, part-of-the-package 'dark era,' Big Bang theorists posit the earliest stars as massive enough to generate ultraviolet radiation. Why? Because ultraviolet rays, if present, conceivably could expel 90 percent of the electrons in the cosmos away from myriad protons they had already bonded with post-Big Bang.

"BBC theorists call that early period of time 'the era of decoupling.' A huge majority of electrons—decoupled from protons and massively expelled from stars due to ultraviolet radiation emanating from within those stars—were forced to roam interstellar space. That same ultraviolet radiation was also able,

BBC theorists claim, to ionize most of the residual hydrogen which was still adrift in space *between* those same massive stars.

"Actually, filling the gaps between those massive stars with expelled electrons doesn't solve BBC's dark era problem. Which inevitable glitch are those experts overlooking?" Kaidan teased.

James saw the correct answer but—numbed by the embarrassment Kaidan was inflicting on him and on cosmologists everywhere—he felt too abashed to speak. Homer was not so reticent. Taking a microphone, Homer gamely replied:

"BBC's electrons were expelled only to be *trapped* in the gaps between those massive UV-emitting stars. Expelled electrons had no starless space to disperse in! Inevitably, of course, BBC's big electron-expelling stars began exploding as supernovae (as big stars tend to do much sooner than small stars).

"However, massive stars that lose mass by exploding as supernovae forfeit their ability to sustain enough UV radiation to keep interstellar electrons away from protons teeming in supernova nebulae. Inevitably, electrons roaming between exploding stars would be sure to recombine with zillions of protons dispersing in supernova nebulae. Next generation stars forming in debris left by exploded first-generation stars would still have nothing but the same de-ionized 'dark era' hydrogen to use as fuel."

"Correct, Homer!" Kaidan enjoined. "That is why BBC fails to solve its 'dark era' problem. Moments from now you will hear me explain how the 'Cinderella version' of the 'Option A' cosmological model does not exclude magnetism nor does it run the slightest risk of imposing a dark era upon the early cosmos.

WHY ZERO IONIZATION EXCLUDES MAGNETISM

"Just as gravity always relates to *mass*," Kaidan explained further, "magnetism always relates exclusively to the degree of *ionization* present *within* any given mass. If any given mass contains zero ionized matter, magnetism cannot be present.

"Many ascribe '*electro*magnetism' merely to the flow of electrons from proton to proton within a given mass. Yet even then, ionization is present in the flow. Every time an electron leaps from one atom to the next, the atom it leaves is ionized until another electron in the flow replaces it. Alas for Big Bang Cosmology, its origin model, being completely devoid of ionized mass in its early stage, also leaves its early cosmos dependent upon gravity alone to foster the formation of stars.

"Gravity, as Tyson and Goldsmith frequently complain, is too weak a force, especially when all it has to work with are the two least massive elements, hydrogen and helium. Keep in mind that hydrogen and helium, especially when super-heated and expanding while exploding from a Big Bang under enormous radiation pressure, are both totally averse to being compressed.

"Magnetism, conversely, is much stronger than gravity at close range. Nor is magnetism discouraged by minimal mass. As long as any given mass is strongly *ionized*, magnetism cares little how much mass is present! Consider that a mere bar magnet 'thumbs its nose at' the gravity of something as massive as the earth by easily lifting a coin.

"Big Bang Cosmologists end up obsessing over dark matter because BBC innately excludes magnetism from assisting gravity in the task of forming stars.

"Permit me to cite Tyson and Goldsmith again. In the second chapter of *Origins* they aver:

"...we expect particles and antiparticles to be created in equal numbers, yet we find a cosmos dominated by ordinary particles, which seem...happy without their antiparticles.[12]

"If Tyson and Goldsmith truly believe that charge parity violation assures 'a tiny excess of matter over antimatter,'[13] why does an imbalance of matter over antimatter disturb them? Do they doubt 'charge parity violation' after all? As I will soon explain, my 'Option A' spares *everyone* from having to wade this mire of impasses. Doubts emerge again as Tyson and Goldsmith continue:

"Do hidden pockets of antimatter in the universe account for the imbalance? Was a law of physics violated...? We may never know the answers to these questions, but for now, if an alien hovers over your front lawn and extends an appendage as a gesture of greeting, toss it your eight ball before you get too friendly.[14]

"In fact *this* alien, who prefers not to be called 'it,' is indeed offering good will to Tyson and Goldsmith and to all mankind."

Bemused chuckles rippled throughout the Symposium and, Kent assumed, among viewers and listeners worldwide as well.

"As one destined to catch the eight ball the good doctors toss via their comments, it falls to me to narrate the true origin of the cosmos, our mutual home. What Tyson and Goldsmith surmise may never be known, I offer to explain here and now to mankind. I promise you an origin model that conforms perfectly to a principle of logic known as Ockham's razor—a rule stating that the *simplest* solution to a mystery takes precedence. Complex solutions must wait in line until simpler solutions fail. It also urges—if unknowns must be postulated—to begin by postulating unknowns that are at least *corollary to knowns*! I will now proceed to unveil my treatise as follows...."

For Kent, James Engle and their many associates, almost palpable anticipation seemed to render the very air in the Forum almost unbreathable. What could Kaidan possibly offer to replace Big Bang cosmology?

Chapter Five
A Uniquely Different Origin

Drawing a deep breath, Kaidan averred: "Just as Big Bang Cosmology's need for six quick fixes marks it as erroneous, so also the origin model I am about to explain is one that has no need to:

1. Meld two billion matter plus antimatter universes to finagle one matter-only cosmos via 'charge parity asymmetry.'
2. Cope with enormous matter-scattering radiation pressure due to that melding.
3. Inexplicably inflate the cosmos at many times the speed of light and then, just as inexplicably, slow all that inflation back down to a pedestrian rate.
4. Conjure up dark matter with not a word about its origin or why anti-dark matter was not needed.
5. Ignore the most outstanding feature of cosmic back-ground radiation: its omni-directionality!
6. Offer an origin model which, due to a total lack of ionization, obliged gravity to form stars with zero help from magnetism—a problem that also guaranteed an incurably persistent dark era.

"To begin: first among Big Bang Cosmology's litany of errors is its implied premise that space and time did not precede the existence of matter and energy. Friends, consider what the non-existence of space and time would require. Non-space denotes absolute *zero location* and non-time denotes absolute *zero duration*. With zero location and zero duration *not even nothing could exist, let alone matter and energy!*

"As I will later explain in more detail, matter—replete with mass, charge, spin, conservation laws and convertibility to energy

—is totally dependent upon both location and duration. Hence the four-dimensional extent continuum (length, width, height and time) had to exist before matter could appear. How long before is part of what I will explain later. For this present moment we will attend to another foundational concept.

THE SPHERE OF ORIGIN AND A 'DOUBLE BUBBLE'

"As I hope we can now agree, positing equal masses of matter and antimatter popping up intermixed at a tiny point cannot account for the 'as is' cosmos around us. So if matter and antimatter did not appear at a tiny point, where else? Only one other option can survive scrutiny. Every bit of matter and antimatter needed for the cosmos had to separate from the inner and outer surfaces of a non-material, *spherical* plane in nothing other than the pre-existent, four-dimensional extent continuum.

"How *huge*, then, did that cosmic sphere have to be? My friends, the **radius** of what we in Arkona call the 'Sphere **of** Origin'—call it 'SOO' for easy reference—stretched out 3.7725 billion light years from its center. Extending that radius on both sides of that 'cosmic center' yields a *diameter* of 7.545 billion light years. Multiply its diameter by the mathematical value of 'pi' (π is 3.14159), and the result is an SOO with a 24-billion-light-year circumference. The formula for the SOO's *surface area*, as every mathematician knows, is $4\pi r^2$. The formula $(4/3)\pi r^3$ yields its *volume*. But now, let me pose two questions to this Symposium. Can anyone here guess which *forms* of mass had to appear on each side of every square micro-millimeter of that vast cosmic sphere? And then, what happened *next*?"

Television cameras swerved immediately from Kaidan to physicist Homer Grassley. Homer, standing bolt upright among his fellow physicists, accepted a microphone from an aisle attendant. Virtually the entire planet heard Homer say, "Sir, I surmise that equal masses of matter and antimatter appeared only to separate immediately—matter from the *inside* and antimatter from the *outside*—of every square millimeter of your posited vast spherical plane we now agree to designate as the 'SOO.'

"Obviously, in this origin model, both masses separated from SOO and from each other with *zero mutual annihilation*. Let me suggest that all the matter was contracting *inwardly* with *clockwise* axial spin abetted by *inbound* dark energy. Likewise all the antimatter was expanding outward with *anticlockwise* axial spin abetted by *outbound* dark energy. Am I correct, Kaidan?"

"I commend you, Dr. Grassley. You are precisely correct!" Kaidan replied, smiling. Again, Kent thought he saw the same momentary facial glow that caught his attention earlier.

"As Dr. Grassley notes," Kaidan affirmed, "the concentric separation of these two spherical masses gave us *two* initially ultra-thin but also ultra-dense cosmic 'bubbles.' One—an *expanding* 'bubble' of *antimatter*—encompassed a *contracting* interior 'bubble' of *matter*. And, as these two masses separated concentrically, *each was spinning oppositely on a common axis running through a very distant and as-yet empty cosmic center!*

THE ANGULAR MOMENTUM FACTOR

"As an expanding sphere, the antimatter bubble became ever more thinly attenuated while slowing its rotation due to conservation of momentum," Kaidan said. "The contracting matter bubble, conversely, was becoming *more and more compacted* while spinning *ever more rapidly* due to conserved angular momentum. As indicated earlier, a colossal 'fling everything back out' phase would inevitably ensue, preventing a so-called 'Big Crunch' at the cosmic center."

Taking one step down from the dais, Kaidan reminisced. "When I was a boy, my father, after teaching me cosmology up to this point, asked me the next most obvious question, and that was, *'Which forms of matter and antimatter* separated from the inside and outside of the sphere of origin, the SOO, to get the cosmos started?'* Before I tell you which answer I gave my father, let me put that same question to you scholars in this gathering. What say you, anyone?"

This time engineer Clyde Smith rose to reply. "Because hydrogen, helium and their antimatter equivalents had to be the first two elements formed," Clyde offered, "Surely proton/

antiproton pairs, along with electron/positron pairs and perhaps neutron/antineutron pairs had to be the first particles to split away from opposite sides of the sphere of origin. Without these key particles, neither hydrogen nor helium nor their antimatter equivalents could form. "

"That is exactly how I answered my father," Kaidan admitted, "but it was the *wrong* answer. Does anyone see why?"

With a flash of insight, George Andrews, one of James Engle's fellow astrophysicists, leaped to his feet. "If protons and electrons had emerged intermixed from the inner surface of the SOO," Dr. Andrews ventured, "their immediate bonding would have yielded 100 percent *atomic* hence *neutral* hydrogen. In that event, Mr. Kaidan, your origin model would have been troubled by a nuisance 'dark era' just as surely as our BBC model is.

"Likewise the resulting absence of ionization would have left gravity just as devoid of magnetism's help in forming stars as gravity is in the BBC model!"

"Dr. Andrew's response is correct, but—" Kaidan said with one eyebrow quizzically raised, "if not protons and electrons, *what else*? And now, with that question, my friends here on Earth, we arrive at the very crux of the true origin story. Who among these 500 scholars will venture to reply?"

THE SERENDIPITOUS HALF-LIFE
OF 'NEUTRONS IN EXCESS'

With that, James, deep in thought, stood to his feet, gripped a microphone and offered a novel response. "All that was needed on the spherical plane now known to us as the SOO," James said, "was for *anti-neutrons* to separate from the SOO's exterior and *neutrons* to separate from the SOO's interior; nothing more."

Everyone in the forum stared at James, mystified. Even Kent, for whom James' comment made no sense, feared that his friend's ego, already bruised to hear Earth's choicest cosmological theory—the Big Bang—so easily and thoroughly discredited, was about to be bruised again if Kaidan dismissed his reply.

"Tell us then, Dr. Engle;" Kaidan pressed, "if the matter bubble, after separating from the inner side of the SOO, consisted only of *neutrons*, where are the *protons* needed to fuel zillions of stars with hydrogen and after that eventually to make heavy elements for planets, moons and comets? And how could *electrons* be found much later to reduce the ionization of elements enough to make planets habitable for flora, fauna and beings like us?"

James replied, "As I'm sure you know, Kaidan, neutrons dislike outnumbering protons. If neutrons are the only form of matter present, or even if neutrons outnumber the protons they are meant to bond with, neutrons begin splitting apart according to a 'free neutron half-life,' a phenomenon in subatomic physics estimated at about 14 minutes. No matter how many neutrons may exceed other forms of matter, *half* of those excess neutrons, over each 14-minute span of time, randomly opt to divide themselves such that neutron after neutron is replaced by three byproducts: *a proton, an electron and one of various kinds of neutrino.*

"Thus neutrons on the plane of the matter 'bubble' began releasing *protons* like bowling balls on or close to the matter plane," James continued. "Also electrons were flying like golf balls partly *on* but mostly away from the inside and outside of the plane. A third by-product, neutrinos, were spraying every which way like high-speed bullets! That is why I think the following had to be true:

1. "The protons and electrons needed to form hydrogen and, later, other elements more complex than hydrogen, became increasingly available as the early minutes of the cosmos elapsed. There would even have been swarms of neutrinos left over as forensic evidence as to how it all occurred! *However:*

2. "As most electrons took flight away from that thin-as-a-neutron matter bubble, the only electrons that slow-moving protons could capture were the *very few* that were released on or close to the plane where protons were proliferating. *Therefore*, I speculate, *almost all of the initial hydrogen automatically ended up ionized and, as a result, magnetism was destined to be there as gravity's partner in what I now believe is the far superior origin model you are presenting here!*

"Now it's my turn to ask: What say *you*, Kaidan?" James asked with a grin.

Kent was relieved to see scientists all around James (and assumedly worldwide) smiling in recognition of what apparently was perfectly logical, if only to them. But what about Kaidan? Did he agree with James' detailed response?

Kaidan smiled spontaneously, saying, "I congratulate you, Dr. Engle, long an ardent advocate of Big Bang Cosmology, for identifying the mechanism that keeps this Sphere of Origin model from falling prey to BBC's magnetism-less 'dark era' problem.

"*Yes!* Provided neutrons were the only kind of matter and were spread evenly on a flat plane rather than jumbled like golf balls in a bag, the free-neutron 14-minute half-life, recognized by physicists worldwide, was guaranteed to release more and more protons, electrons and various kinds of neutrinos over a brief interval. Due to the thinness of the plane, the slowness of heavy protons and the swiftness of tiny electrons, some 90 percent of the latter escaped capture by counterpart protons. Thus only 10 percent of the hydrogen became the relatively opaque atomic variety.

"Many of you realize, of course, that this fortuitous 14-minute half-life applied also to anti-neutrons on the expanding antimatter bubble, where antiprotons, positrons and neutrino equivalents were proliferating at equal rates.

HOW OTHER LIGHT ELEMENTS APPEARED
AMID THE IONIZED HYDROGEN

"How, I ask," Kaidan continued, "did this free-neutron 14-minute half-life also assure that a few other light elements would also appear, interspersed with ionized hydrogen?"

Still feeling relief due to Kaidan's commendation, James stood ready to offer a further reply based on his grasp of physics.

"Kaidan's neutrons-only bubble," James began, "assured that *some* newly-hatched protons would bond with still-intact neutrons to form a heavier form of hydrogen known as **deuterium**. Some of these nuclei in turn, bumping into other still-intact neutrons, bonded with them to form **tritium** and—in greater amounts—**helium** with traces of **lithium**.

"I must add that neutrons, once bonded with protons, are no longer subject to that fortuitous 14-minute half-life. That half-life is cancelled forever as long as neutrons remain bonded with protons.

"So, within about three hours after the appearance of the 'double bubble,'" James concluded, "the 14-minute half-life of free neutrons transformed a neutrons-only matter bubble into one where the only neutrons left were the minority that bonded with newly released protons to form deuterium, tritium, helium and lithium."

"Indeed!" Kaidan exclaimed, as if co-discovering a momentous insight with James. "By then, at least 90 percent of the electrons released would have escaped—45 percent *outside* the matter bubble and 45 percent *inside*! The only electrons captured by protons would have been, as Dr. Engle said, the 10 percent or so that were released so close to meandering protons that their capture was inevitable.

"Thus 90 percent of SOO electrons, unlike BBC electrons, escaped prior to star formation and had vast volumes of inner and outer space to roam in until, eons later, the inner 45 percent would be direly needed to de-ionize planetary matter in nebulae. In fact, ionized hydrogen *still* surpasses neutral H by approximately the same magnetism-assuring 9-to-1 ratio. And further proton-neutron bonding to form deuterium, tritium and helium did indeed preserve *some* neutrons for posterity before that ongoing 14-minute half-life had time to deconstruct every free-state neutron."

Descending the stairway from the dais, Kaidan turned toward James Engle and beamed a smile of approval.

"Everyone, please join me in lauding Dr. Engle for his accurate perceptions." A groundswell of response surrounded James as he resumed his seat, his face aglow with an awe that comes only when a flood of new insight summarily abolishes competing options.

Indeed, the entire process James had described with a little prompting by Kaidan, Kent now realized, provided more than enough ionized hydrogen intermixed with traces of helium for all the stars and elements that would ever form. Kent felt pleased as never before that he, a theologian, and an astrophysicist like James, could be friends.

CLYDE'S FLASH OF INSIGHT

Suddenly Clyde Smith rose to interject a question: "Excuse me, Kaidan, Sir! Granted that neutrons and anti-neutrons separated oppositely from the SOO with zero mutual annihilation, what about neutrinos and antineutrinos that were also being scattered while the 14-minute half-life of free neutrons and anti-neutrons was releasing *them* in all directions? I'm guessing at least some neutrinos and antineutrinos—vectored toward each other and flying almost at light speed—overcame the widening of the gap between the matter and antimatter bubbles and mutually annihilated each other at various points in that intervening space.

"If that happened, Sir, would not part of the energy released by their melding even now be reaching the rest of the cosmos omni-directionally? I ask you, is this at least part of what enables your superior cosmology to explain why CBR, the cosmic background radiation, is arriving everywhere omni-directionally?"

For an answer, Kaidan pointed to all seven screens with a congratulatory grin. Clyde and the entire Symposium saw Clyde's own on-the-spot verbal explanation unfolding visually on all seven screens! Everyone saw symbols depicting neutrinos and anti-neutrinos meeting and converting each other entirely to photons with some of the photons radiating in toward distant galaxies.

"You are so correct, Clyde," Kaidan said.

The entire gathering stood to its feet to join Kaidan in applauding George Andrews, James and Clyde. Clyde, who had given Kaidan a single wrong answer, had redeemed himself.

"Although it would take longer," Kaidan appended, "even many electrons *outbound* from the matter sphere would eventually meld between the two bubbles with positrons *inbound* from the antimatter sphere. Their mutual annihilation was destined to yield even more omni-directional energy than almost massless neutrinos and antineutrinos could yield."

At that point Kaidan launched the following contrast.

"Scrapping Big Bang Cosmology and replacing it with the Sphere of Origin model, we have no need to co-create and then co-annihilate 2 billion universes somehow crowded together at a tiny point! Nor do we have the slightest need for charge parity violation! Nor does an infant cosmos need to cope with incalculable radiation pressure! Nor do we need to inflate and then brake the cosmos so as to cheat gravity and disperse the heat! Nor do we need to conjure up origin-less dark matter! Nor do we have difficulty explaining the omni-directionality of CBR! Nor do we end up with zero ionization and gravity devoid of magnetism as a viable partner!

"Ladies and gentlemen and young people worldwide, does the principle of logic I mentioned earlier, Ockham's razor, strongly favor my Sphere of Origin model? Is not *inbound* dark energy, for example, an unknown that is perfectly corollary to the *outbound* version of the present cosmos?"

Wavelike, the forum surged upright with applause.

Earlier, with Kaidan adroitly dismantling Big Bang Cosmology, psychiatrist Justine Hobbs had noticed embarrassed resentment clouding the faces of several leading specialists on that topic. Dr. James Engle had been one such person. Justine even winced with concern that James—if he opted to confront Kaidan with an angry obstructionist protest—might precipitate an interstellar incident on Day 1 of the Symposium.

Now, Justine could only admire how adroitly Kaidan had persuaded scientists whose best theories he had refuted minutes before to participate agreeably by helping him explain key points of Arkona's far superior origin model. At times, Kaidan appeared to be just standing by, posing question after question as if he were the one needing to be taught cosmology! Surely that strategy was helping to salve otherwise bruised egos.

To ease the pain others were feeling, Kaidan had even admitted his own failure as a child to respond correctly when tested by his father about cosmology. *Kaidan,* Justine texted to everyone on the Loop, *is nothing less than an interstellar Socrates with remarkable ability to teach simply by asking questions.*

"Let me now illustrate on all seven screens," Kaidan resumed, "what Dr. Engle has already envisioned so cogently."

Descending to audience level, Kaidan faced all seven screens. As he clicked a handheld device, a thin blue line spanned all seven screens. Kaidan announced it as representing "the plane of the SOO, the sphere of origin."

With a second click, Kaidan added two rows of symbols simulating antineutrons above and neutrons below the blue line. With a third click, Kaidan's respective rows of 'antineutrons' and 'neutrons' separated from each other above and below the blue line. As they parted, individual neutrons and antineutrons began 'bursting' at random distances from each other and on alternate screens, thus simulating the 14-minute half-life of free neutrons and antineutrons. Kaidan was employing all seven screens as a unit to simulate the eight-billion-light-year diameter of the SOO.

Speedy electrons and much speedier neutrinos were leaving slow-moving protons wallowing amid still-intact neutrons on the plane of the matter bubble. Bursting antineutrons were also releasing equivalent byproducts above and below the plane of the antimatter bubble. Everyone recognized that the distance between such widely scattered release events guaranteed that relatively few protons and electrons would find each other to form neutral atomic hydrogen, the opaque kind. Instead, ionized hydrogen was proliferating large-scale. Arko-cosmology did indeed avoid a nuisance "dark era." It also guaranteed that magnetism would be there ready to work from Day 1 onward!

Next Kaidan utilized his seven-screen array to depict occasional newly hatched protons bonding with still intact neutrons to form deuterium, tritium, helium and lithium in that order. He also displayed parallel processes involving anti-neutrons, antiprotons on the antimatter sphere forming 90 percent ionized anti-hydrogen, 10 percent atomic anti-hydrogen along with anti-deuterium, anti-tritium, anti-helium and anti-lithium as well.

That done, Kaidan ascended the steps back to his podium and turned to face the Symposium and his worldwide audience anew. "From this point on," he declared, "I will be narrating a sequence of events that occurred on and within the spherical matter bubble. Please keep in mind that parallel events were occurring in the exterior antimatter realm. Remember also that the expansion of the antimatter 'bubble' deprived it of a variety of benefits that were fully available to the matter cosmos merely by the fact that the matter cosmos was continuously *contracting* throughout its initial phase.

"I will now narrate how those various benefits ensued."

With that, Kaidan drew a deep breath and strode forward to the very edge of the speaker's platform.

Chapter Six
Magnetism, Gravity's Co-Star!

"With the formation of enormous quantities of *ionized* hydrogen plus lesser amounts of *ionized* helium and trace amounts of *ionized* deuterium, tritium and lithium," Kaidan commented, "inevitably, zillions of magnetic fields formed everywhere on that vast, ever-spinning yet also *contracting* matter sphere.

"Every magnetic field's negative pole of course drew in as many protons as it could attract. Every positive pole, conversely, was just as avidly eager to attract free electrons, *of which virtually none were available*! Ninety percent of the electrons released by neutron decay had fled much too far outside or much too far inside the matter sphere to be drawn back. The other 10 percent of all the electrons were now concertedly orbiting protons; hence that 10 percent could not be magnetically attracted.

"Worldwide audience, try to imagine how enormous the ensuing magnetic imbalance was!" Kaidan began. "Magnetic fields expect to attract approximately equal numbers of positive and negative particles to their respective poles. In the early cosmos, that was not possible! Immediately after the matter cosmos detached from the antimatter cosmos at the Sphere of Origin, the negative pole of every field became saturated with protons while every positive pole remained virtually if not completely electron-less. Yet this proved not to be a crisis after all for the zillions of imbalanced magnetic fields due to the following.

MAGNETIC FIELD REVERSALS:
A STUDIOUSLY UNRECOGNIZED FACTOR

"Just as neutrons in excess undo the excess via their 14-minute half-life, magnetic fields also have a handy way of keeping one pole from becoming excessively overloaded. Imbalanced magnetic fields simply *reverse their polarity*; and when magnetic fields reverse polarity, whatever is concentrated at just one pole is forcefully expelled as a jet straight out from that pole.

"When a magnetic field in clouds above the earth amasses too many electrons at one pole and few if any protons at the other pole—zap! Both poles reverse, causing dangerous streams of excess electrons to flash forcefully as lightning, usually from sky to ground!

"Likewise, magnetic field reversals on the surface of the Sun forcefully hurl masses of ionized plasma—solar flares—out into space. Whereas most lightning on Earth is an electron-related event, solar flares are what could well be termed 'proton lightning.' As awesome as lightning made of electrons can be, the fact that each proton packs more than 1836 times as much mass as each electron makes *proton lightning* vastly more awesome!

"As proof that solar flares occur when magnetic poles reverse," Kaidan said, "consider: matter expelled from a magnetic pole on the Sun in the form of a solar flare is matter that had to be attracted to that pole initially. So if a negative magnetic pole on the Sun attracts positive ions and then ejects them, that negative pole, by definition, has become a positive pole. But now let me explain on-screen what happens to a *majority* of solar flares.

Kaidan, showing a photo of an arcing solar flare on-screen, said, "See! Positive plasma is expelled when a negative pole on the Sun suddenly becomes a positive pole. Then, as soon as that positive mass begins its outbound journey, the same negative pole attracts it *back*, but not back to where that pole *was*. Rather, it is drawn to that pole's *new* location at a site situated thousands of miles away from where that negative pole had been! That is why a majority of solar flares *'change their minds' and arc back toward the Sun!* More powerfully ejected flares escape the Sun.

"Do terra-scientists really understand that solar fares are caused by actual magnetic field reversals (MFRs)? Well, they do know that the Sun itself flips its *overall* polarity approximately every eleven years. Yet when it comes to solar flares, author Dr. Raman Prinja, for example, a researcher and lecturer in the U.K., avers only that solar flares convert...

"…enormous amounts to magnetic energy to launch material into space at millions of kilometers per hour.[15]

"Thus everyone sees that magnetism is involved but fails to see magnetic field reversals as the actual mechanism at work.

"Magnetic field reversals occur in minor ways, too. Tiny magnetic field reversals can cause people to **sneeze**, an event that enables an adult to expel matter at 35 to 40 miles per hour."

Everyone in the Symposium gaped in amazement at Kaidan. Kent imagined the same reaction spreading worldwide as Kaidan continued. "The United States Navy has developed a 'rail gun,' a weapon that exploits magnetic field reversals (MFRs) to shoot projectiles as far as 60 nautical miles or more. That is at least nine times as far as chemical explosives can hurl projectiles. Such weapons are already mounted on so-called Zumwalt ships.

"Also, in 2015 NASA launched a satellite called 'The Magnetospheric Multiscale (MMS) Mission.' Its purpose: to study explosions of energy in Earth's magnetic field.

"Now that Earth science is on the threshold of recognizing magnetic field reversals as a commonplace and even usable phenomenon, surely mankind is also ready to appreciate what a major force magnetic field reversals were at the launching of the cosmos. Let me now explain what transpired.

HOW MAGNETISM PREPPED
THE COSMOS FOR GRAVITY

"Listeners everywhere," Kaidan continued apace, "no matter how textbook-y this sounds, it is something you need to try to understand. Try to imagine zillions of ionized protons in the early cosmos becoming concentrated (all with zero help from gravity, by the way) at a zillion negative magnetic poles. Protons repel each other, of course; yet negative magnetic poles override their mutual repulsion enough to keep protons packed together despite their natural propensity to fly apart. That override fails, however, when a magnetic field reaches a critical level of imbalance. At that moment, *fields reverse their poles as follows.*

"When a negative magnetic pole becomes lavishly endowed with protons while the positive pole in the same field garners few if any electrons, the field automatically switches poles so as to redress the imbalance. A positive magnetic pole, suddenly juxtaposed against a mass of positive protons, immediately expels them very forcefully! Inasmuch as the positive pole has no electrons to expel, conservation of momentum requires the positive pole—in lieu of expelling electrons—to push *itself* away from where it had been.

"It's as if imbalanced magnetic fields exploit excess protons as 'rocket fuel' to remove themselves to places where perhaps they can attract protons *and* electrons *equally!* Yet in the infant cosmos, regardless of where magnetic fields ended up, they still found nothing but more protons to amass and expel and amass and expel repeatedly in multiple directions.

"So zillions of negative magnetic poles in the infant cosmos suddenly became *positive* magnetic poles saturated with protons, protons being the very thing positive poles are meant to *repel.* Imagine every *dyne* of pent-up mutual repulsion amid the protons themselves not only becoming kinetic but also being *abetted kinetically* by the even stronger repulsive force of the positive pole itself! Zillions of blobs of expelled protons began flying in all directions with lightning-like force.

"To put it mildly," Kaidan sighed satirically, "*the entire matter cosmos became* **a colossal storm filled with nothing less than proton lightning!** Imagine myriad solar flares—despite the absence of yet-to-be stars—forcefully expelling masses of ionized hydrogen/helium plasma all across and out from the plane of a steadily thickening matter sphere!

"You all know the dictum: a moving object proceeds by its own momentum *in a straight line* unless another force intervenes. Take matter expelled by supernova explosions, for example. It disperses initially along straight-line radii, just as we expect. Later, however, that same matter begins *zigzagging* in different directions, as we will see in several photos of supernovae debris fields. As surely as that expelled matter is heavily ionized, magnetic field reversals are indeed becoming 'another force that intervenes.' They keep altering the otherwise straight-line momenta of ionized matter into seemingly crazy zigzag patterns. I say 'seemingly crazy,' because those zigzag motions served to concentrate masses of hydrogen enough to activate gravity for the final phase in the formation of first-generation stars. Later I will present photos proving that masses of heavier matter expelled when first-generation stars began exploding as supernovae are still tracing zigzag courses that result in the formation of a second generation of new entities in the cosmos. But for now...

"In addition to magnetic field reversals (MFRs), something else was happening. Everything in the matter sphere was becoming ever more compressed by the contraction of the matter bubble, which was itself abetted by dark energy's large-scale *contraction* within the matter cosmos itself.

MAGNETISM AND GRAVITY—AIDED BY DARK ENERGY IN REVERSE—COMPACTED STARS!

"As surely as dark energy kept abetting the shrinkage of the spinning matter sphere's spherical surface area, mobile proton blobs—already randomly crowded in some locations by very forceful MFRs—became even more crowded due to that overall contraction. Soon, myriad centers of mass became concentrated enough to activate **gravity** as magnetism's latent team player.

"Yielding at last to sufficiently strengthened gravity, ever more massive proton blobs began at last to be attracted toward centers of mass rather than simply bypassing them. Ongoing accretions eventually enabled gravity to pull in even orbiting masses. As more and more centers of mass merged, intensified gravity triggered **nuclear fusion**. What began as zigzagging proton masses ultimately coalesced as hosts of glowing *stars*!

"Just as swarms of electron-less protons led to reversing magnetic fields on the actual plane of the matter sphere, so also swarms of proton-less electrons led to the same phenomenon far inside and also far outside the matter sphere. Seeing that blobs of protons became *proton stars*, why do we not also have blobs of *electrons* coalescing and merging to form *electron stars*?

"Protons, being 1836.12 times as massive as electrons, wake gravity up. Massed electrons let gravity nap. Now you know why magnetism has to be so strong up close, gravity strong enough far away, protons so heavy and electrons so light!

"After coalescing stars initially with ionized hydrogen and helium, gravity drew in and added the other 10 percent of matter—the electrically neutral *atomic* hydrogen and helium—to the initial stellar masses. This trend moderated the ionization of many stars to a degree. This process continued gradually over eons of time.

ANOTHER SOURCE FOR OMNI-DIRECTIONAL CBR

"Be aware also that each magnetic field reversal [MFR], in addition to expelling ionized *protons*, also emitted a blast of high-energy *photons*, many of which radiated toward regions of space where galaxies like ours would later exist. This very high energy radiation, modified over time by the distance travelled and the later emergence of today's dark energy in reverse, was destined to contribute significantly to what I have already mentioned as **the cosmic background radiation**, which I will hereafter designate as simply **'CBR.'**

"Now do you understand, my friends, why CBR is coming to us *omni-directionally*? CBR did not radiate from one point, as Big Bang Cosmology purports, but from the all-encompassing matter bubble—a source that enclosed the matter cosmos."

A sigh of wonder arose from within the Symposium.

"Stars formed in the very early cosmos," Kaidan added," are known to astronomers here on Earth and in other star systems as 'first-generation stars.' Now let me explain how these myriad first-generation stars, even as they were being formed, became divided into a variety of stellar categories known as **globular clusters, elliptical galaxies** and **halo stars**.

THE TEN-EIGHTY-TEN RATIO

"On far-away Arkona we refer to a factor known as the **'Ten-Eighty-Ten Ratio.'** Very simply, with zillions of stars coalescing on the matter sphere, approximately *one out of ten* newborn stars in that vast spherical host **became vectored more or less directly toward the very distant cosmic center**. Keep in mind that the then-current *contraction* of the entire matter sphere (the *in*-phase of dark energy) was also continuously abetting the motion of these out-in-front, 10 percent, first-generation stars directly toward the cosmic center.

"This inward-leading 10 percent of the total number of stars—moving toward the cosmic center ever more rapidly than everything else—were also, on average, converging closer to each other more rapidly as well. Consequently, it ensued that gravity began clumping these 'inward-leading 10 percent stars' around random centers of mass that happened to form in their midst. As a result, these discrete, gravitationally linked stellar clumps became **globular clusters**, most of which consisted of a few tens of thousands of stars."

Next, Kaidan—displaying photos of typical globular clusters of stars—commented, "Whereas globular clusters exhibit anywhere from tens of thousands to a few million stars [see 'A' in the photo section], elliptical galaxies may contain at least 100 billion such stars. Now let me explain how our 'ten-eighty-ten ratio' accounts for entities as massive as elliptical galaxies.

"Meanwhile, back on the range, so to speak, the middle 80 percent or so of our zillions of first-generation stars were those that happened to be vectored, on average, **more or less *crosswise* and *up or down* relative to the still very distant cosmic center**. Even while lagging behind the globular cluster stars, these '80 percent stars' were also being drawn closer to the cosmic center as well as closer to each other due to both gravity and the overall contraction of the matter sphere.

Over time, these '80 percent stars'—increasingly crowded together due to the radially inward pull of dark energy and drawn together by gravity—converged to form very much larger masses around gravitationally linked centers of mass—i.e., they became **elliptical galaxies**!

"Stars concentrated near the middle of the 80 percent mass formed the largest elliptical galaxies. Those that formed between them and the globular clusters became mid-size elliptical galaxies. Those that coalesced in the outermost part of the 80 percent group became rather dwarfish elliptical galaxies. Other galaxies in that further-out region assumed irregular forms.

"In Big Bang Cosmology, matter was far too attenuated to form anything as massive as a galaxy unless a super-massive 'black hole' formed first and caused massive amounts of matter to spiral in around it. That solution fails, of course, because black holes could not form unless galaxies with enough mass to form 'black holes' were already there!

"Indeed, galaxies formed with no need for black holes or dark matter at all. Don't you see? Just as the Big Bang needed dark matter to compensate for the absence of magnetism, so also Big Bang Cosmology needs 'black holes' to compensate for its lack of an early phase in which dark energy and gravity teamed up to pull already formed stars *inward* to form the stellar communities we know as globular clusters and elliptical galaxies.

"What, then, befell the last 10 percent or so of those zillions of stars?" Kaidan queried. "Ah, yes; those 'last 10 percent stars' emerged from that early cosmic 'shooting gallery' on **trajectories vectored directly away from the cosmic center**. Dark energy was still drawing those 'final 10 percent stars' ever closer to the cosmic center, but they were still much too dispersed to form gravitationally linked stellar clumps. These uniquely lonely 'last 10 percent stars' would later be known as *halo stars*!

"Thus first-generation stars fell into just three categories: elliptical galaxies, globular clusters and halo stars. Some elliptical galaxies, ages later, would begin expelling jets of stars to form external spiral arms. More about those galaxies later.

GSISC: GRAVITY SHARED IN STELLAR COMMUNITY

"A huge majority of first-generation stars," Kaidan averred, "being clumped together to form globular clusters and elliptical galaxies, were all destined to age slower than halo stars due to what I call **GSISC: gravity shared in stellar community**. This new phrase signifies that gravity in globular clusters and elliptical galaxies never acts exclusively on behalf of any one star in such systems. In that kind of communal context, gravity becomes conflicted as follows.

"The gravitational pull of multiple nearby stars reduces the amount of *inward* pressure local gravity would otherwise exert on the core of any one star in a globular cluster or an elliptical galaxy! Thus gravity pressures the cores of these clustered stars just enough to convert hydrogen to helium but at slower rates. That pressure, however, is not forceful enough to fuse light-mass nuclei together to make medium-mass or heavy elements.

"Thus greater numbers of protons are free to share in basic helium-making fusion for longer periods. That is why, apart from intrusive disruptions, heavy-element-rich novae and supernovae (discussed later) do not occur in globular clusters nor in elliptical galaxies nor even in the nuclei of spiral arm galaxies.

"Ergo, stars in globular clusters and elliptical galaxies get to shine for extra ages without fusing the heavy elements needed to make planets, moons and comets. Their inability to fuse heavy elements explains why opaque heavy-element nebulae seen in the lenticular disks and spiral arms of many galaxies almost never appear in globular clusters, in elliptical galaxies, or even in the *nuclei* of spiral arm galaxies. Their inability to fuse heavy elements also means that such stars, apart from intrusive disruption, lack the heavy elements needed to form solar systems.

"Conversely, the relative isolation of individual halo stars frees them from the restraint of gravity shared in stellar community. Halo star gravity pressures the cores of this special category of stars enough to convert hydrogen to helium and, more than that, to fuse helium nuclei as middle-mass elements. This of course happens at a rate proportional to the mass of each halo star. This factor shortens the 'lifespan' of halo stars for reasons I have yet to explain."

James texted: *I thought by now K's logic would have let slip a flaw or two. To my awe, that just isn't happening.*

Pointing an electronic control to all seven screens, Kaidan displayed a series of photographs of galaxies, some of which were girdled by rings of matter labeled as **'lenticular disks.'** Others featured **spiral arms** emanating from opposite sides of their central mass.

"A short while ago," Kaidan reminded the Symposium, "I explained how the 'ten-eighty-ten ratio' divided myriad first-generation stars into three *separate* categories: globular clusters, elliptical galaxies and halo stars. After a brief break, I will explain what caused many elliptical galaxies to sprout various kinds of spiral arms. After that I must also explain what caused globular clusters and halo stars—all of which were formed not only apart from elliptical galaxies but also apart from each other—to end up orbiting around galaxies of any and all shapes and sizes. Three successive developments, all integral to the cosmology known in the 24-planet Federation, must be credited as enhancing galaxies to such a fine-tuned degree of complexity."

With that, Kaidan turned and walked away into a wing of the platform.

Joining Charles Stein at a coffee urn, Kent said, "May I ask you a personal question?"

"Permission granted," Stein replied.

"At what age did you become an atheist and what was the precipitating factor, if any?"

Stein's brow furrowed amid steam rising from his cup. "You theists like to assume," he claimed, "that atheism has to be triggered by a tragic event, such as bitterness due to the death of a loved one. For me, at 20 years of age, I simply perceived that the universe keeps operating in its own self-contained way. It needs no fine-tuning from anything exterior to itself. I concluded that the cosmos has no need of God, so neither do I need him. The cosmos is all there is and all I need, period!"

With that, Stein turned and walked away from Kent.

Chapter Seven
Enhancing Elliptical Galaxies

"Elliptical galaxies become altered," Kaidan resumed, "when galactic-scale magnetic pole reversals (Mfrs) happen in their overall magnetic fields. As Mfrs kept jettisoning masses of ionized gas until stars coalesced wherever masses of that gas happened to reach critical density, so also, eons later, galactic-scale Mfrs began expelling huge numbers of fully-formed first-generation stars straight out into space! This happens when too many stars with high levels of positive charge crowd so close to a galaxy's negative magnetic pole that they trigger a massive MFR. Inevitably, expelled stars form a long jet streaming out from one side of a typical elliptical galaxy.

"What I'm describing now is the galactic equivalent of a solar flare, except in this case hosts of stars are being expelled from a galaxy rather than mere *plasma* from just one *star*.

"No sooner do expelled stars begin their outbound journey than the magnetic pole that expelled them—having switched to the opposite side of the same galaxy—begins drawing a host of other *positively* charged stars closer and closer to its new location. Eventually a *second* MFR launches *them* as a second stream of stars jettisoned from the opposite side of the same galaxy.

"Though these opposite expulsions are consecutive, they appear simultaneous as viewed from Earth. Terra-astronomers refer to such events as inexplicable 'bipolar outflows,' perhaps based on the assumption that they occur simultaneously.

"As these *two* trails of stars begin to lag behind the ongoing rotation of what is no longer an elliptical galaxy, two options emerge. First, if expelled stars lag *close enough* to the expelling host as it rotates, they *engirdle* the host's interior with what terra-astronomers designate as a 'lenticular disk.' More forceful ejections, conversely, yield trails of stars that encircle galaxies at increasing distances from opposite sides of the expelling galaxy's rotating core. The result is what is known here on Earth as 'spiral galaxies' [See 'B' in the photo section].

"Each expulsion shrinks the mass remaining in the galactic core. If a third and a fourth MFR ensue, a diminished nucleus will have *four* spiraling arms attached. Each expulsion alters the rate at which the remaining core rotates.

"Now let me ask, Is anyone here ready to affirm why—in terms of physical laws I have already explained—all of the stars jettisoned to form lenticular disks or spiral arms will no longer be subject to GSISC? That, if you recall, is an acrostic for 'gravity shared in stellar community.'"

Kaidan paced back and forth, awaiting a response.

Mentally reviewing and applying the basics of Kaidan's cosmology, James Engle stood to reply. TV cameras swiveled to record for posterity whatever he might say. Kent saw both James and Kaidan featured split-screen on all seven screens.

WHY GSISC NO LONGER AFFECTS EXPELLED STARS

"First let me say," James began, "how amazed I am that I did not recognize these polar outflows as adding lenticular disks and spiral arms to former elliptical galaxies. Photos of galaxies yield evidence enough! What you say is true, Kaidan; BBC's exclusion of magnetism and especially its failure to recognize MFRs blinds us to conclusions that become obvious once the role of magnetism and MFRs is recognized. Thank you, Sir, for freeing me and—I hope—all of us from BBC bias. Now to reply:

"Earlier, Kaidan, you explained that gravity shared in stellar community prevents such stars from fusing light gases to make heavy elements. You also explained that if such stars cannot fuse heavy elements—elements needed to make planets—neither can in-community stars be found hosting planets."

Kent and Justine smiled to see hundreds of listeners focusing attention on whatever James might say in response.

"However, I'm guessing," James continued, "that when galaxies experiencing an MFR syndrome 'sneeze' stars far out into empty space, each such star has its own gravity all to itself. Hence such stars begin at once to fuse the heavy elements needed to form planets, moons and comets.

"How am I doing?" James asked his august instructor.

"All you say is correct," Kaidan said with a smile. Then, facing the large gathering, he continued with further comments.

A WIDER HABITAT FOR PLANETS

"I want everyone to understand what Dr. Engle so ably describes. Greater isolation from other stars in the less-crowded environment of a lenticular disk or a spiral arm frees gravity in each expelled star to do what gravity in halo stars has long been doing: fusing helium nuclei to make *heavier elements*!

"When heavy elements reach critical mass in a star, a star explodes immediately, only to recover and then explode again via processes I have yet to describe. Heavy elements, ejected from an exploding star, cool and then coalesce to form *planets*—some of which eventually become habitats suitable for life. Others form moons and comets."

Engineer Clyde Smith raised his hand. Kaidan nodded and Smith asked, "Sir, once stars relocate to more amenable sites in lenticular disks or spiral arms, *how long* does it take for these previously quiescent stars to explode as supernovae?"

"Actually, they begin exploding almost at once, astronomically speaking," Kaidan replied, "and here is why.

"The moment galactic-strength magnetic poles reverse right under the chins of what you poetically dub as 'quiescent stars,' Dr. Smith, can you imagine what happens?

"Why, the very force of such powerful magnetic field reversals temporarily compresses the spherical mass of pole-proximate stars until they resemble *pumpkins* for several minutes. During that brief period, pressure several magnitudes greater than gravity alone could ever exert upon a stellar core fuses hydrogen and helium nuclei together until **heavier elements** emerge profusely. *Every star thus becomes almost instantly 'pregnant' with a 'fetus' of heavy elements in its womb.*

"As the expulsion diminishes, stars rebound back to and beyond their ideal shape until, briefly, they resemble rather elongated gourds, which transition imposes a *second* blitz of extreme pressure on their cores.

"Be assured, Clyde! By the time each ejected star becomes spherical again, whether in the context of a lenticular disk or a spiral arm, that star is soon more than ready to disperse its lode of heavy elements by exploding as either a nova or a supernova.

"And that is why billions of nebulae, all of them rich with heavy-element plasmas and clouds of opaque dust, begin darkening lenticular disks and spiral arms *almost as quickly* as disks and arms form. Apart from the intense squeeze generated by galactic-strength magnetic reversals, heavy elements in galactic disks and arms would appear at a much slower pace.

"Look at these examples on my seven screens! Bands of stars dark with heavy elements do not appear in globular clusters or elliptical galaxies unless two or more such have collided.

"That is also why, at the cost of a much shorter lifespan, some disk stars and spiral arm stars—spewing heavy elements in the throes of 'going nova'—endow neighboring stars with the privilege of hosting solar systems and perhaps even living communities! Later I will explicitly describe how that happens.

"Now let me describe a second phenomenon, one that has enhanced virtually all galaxies in a very special way.

HOW GALAXIES GAINED GLOBULAR CLUSTERS AS SATELLITES

"Almost without exception," Kaidan explained, "globular clusters and halo stars—despite having formed not only apart from each other but also apart from galaxies—are now found orbiting profusely around elliptical, lenticular and spiral arm galaxies. How then did galaxies acquire so many outriders that were not present when the galaxies themselves formed amid that middle 80 percent or so of the first stars?

"Big Bang cosmologists claim that globular clusters and halo stars formed from the same rotating clouds of gas that birth galaxies. If that were so, the rotation of each such cloud of gas would predetermine the angular momentum of a galaxy plus the angular momentum of the globular clusters and halo stars in orbit around a galaxy.

"But such an explanation fails to solve a major problem. Though every star in a spiral galaxy has its own individual motion, generically all the stars in any given galaxy share a common angular momentum by orbiting *around the central axis* of a galaxy once every several million years or so.

"Globular clusters and halo stars, conversely—unlike stars that are native to a galaxy—orbit galaxies at eccentric angles and in odd directions. Each globular cluster and halo star *has its own unique angular momentum!*

"This means that globular clusters and halo stars, as I explained earlier, were not birthed in the same gas clouds that birthed galaxies. Rather, they coalesced in sparser, smaller gas clouds and were captured subsequently by the gravity of galaxies. The angles at which globular clusters and halo stars orbit galaxies trace back to the trajectories that brought them close enough to galaxies to be captured by their gravity.

"Big Bang Cosmology's hypothetical mega-blast, followed by Guth's equally hypothetical mega-inflation, generated such *extreme* dispersions of matter that Big Bang theorists, even with hypothetical 'dark matter,' cannot explain how globular clusters and halo stars coalesced *apart from each other*, let alone *apart from galaxies*. Nor can they explain what subsequently returned globular clusters and halo stars close enough to galaxies to be captured by them despite their radially outbound expansion in the BBC model.

"As I will now reveal, cosmology as recognized everywhere in the 24-planet Federation has no problem explaining the sequence of events that enabled galaxies to capture globular clusters and halo stars *both*."

Kaidan, scanning his audience, asked: "Are you all anticipating what comes *next* in this saga of cosmic origin?"

Much to Stanfield's surprise, dozens of adults suddenly began whispering among themselves like excited teens, brimming with anticipation. One of them found the courage to rise and shout aloud, "The great cosmic 'fling it all back out!' Kaidan, you have yet to tell us how *that* happened!"

Yet Stanfield had to admit that he, too, was engrossed, albeit much more reservedly. Kaidan, meanwhile, had turned away to post his own title for that very event across his seven-screen array:

THE GREAT COSMIC CONFLUENCE

"Whereas globular clusters formed out in front of inbound elliptical galaxies," Kaidan reminded his audience, "halo stars coalesced while lagging *far behind* inbound elliptical galaxies. How then did natural cosmic processes enable far-ahead globular clusters and far-behind halo stars to get close enough to elliptical galaxies to be captured by their gravity? Indeed, it gives me great pleasure now to explain how that happened," Kaidan promised with a luminous smile and a wink.

"Eon after eon, the innermost layer of the matter sphere, teeming with first-to-arrive globular clusters, kept contracting ever nearer to the cosmic center. Still, by the time the innermost globular clusters had closed to within some **1.4 billion light years of the cosmic center**, the matter sphere's reservoir of conserved angular momentum had already begun side-shifting every globular cluster's trajectory very significantly.

"In addition, *inbound* dark energy by then had newly switched to *outbound*! So dark energy's first-ever outbound thrust began abetting conserved angular momentum's power to deflect globular cluster trajectories. Myriad globular clusters—barred from getting nearer to the cosmic center—inevitably began angling *away* from the cosmic center.

"That, of course, launched every globular cluster on a collision course toward an encompassing mass of billions of galaxies that were all *still inbound*!

"The inbound momentum of myriad galaxies, you see, had not yet been slowed by dark energy's reversal. That reversal, initiated nearer to the cosmic center, was just beginning to progress outward. And conserved angular momentum had not fully redirected the galaxies' trajectories at that time.

"Soon zillions of globular clusters, colliding with galaxies only to be captured by their gravity, found themselves hugging their captors' flanks and shoulders—like minnows swarming around whales. Yet each globular cluster was now orbiting its captor according to the unique angle of approach that first brought it within reach of the galaxy's gravity.

"This galaxy of ours—which you call 'The Milky Way'— captured approximately 200 globular clusters at that time.

"Now it was the galaxies' turn. With captive globular clusters hanging on, more and more galaxies began to be deflected away on increasingly oblique trajectories due to conserved angular momentum. That deflected momentum was abetted by an ever-strengthening amplitude of *outbound* dark energy!

"What then did these first-to-arrive galaxies meet as, laden with quantities of newly acquired globular clusters, they began rebounding away from the cosmic center?" Kaidan asked whimsically. "Of course! They began mingling with later-arriving galaxies, many of which were just beginning to acquire their share of globular clusters. Collisions were inevitable, collisions that could not have happened in Big Bang Cosmology's explosively expanding and, on top of that, even hyper-*inflating* cosmos!"

Kaidan paused to flick a series of photos of colliding galaxies across all seven screens, all of them oddly bent out of shape as a result of long-ago collisions. Kent saw many listeners nodding as they grasped not only how galaxies amassed globular clusters but also why galactic collisions happened more frequently than Big Bang Cosmology could have predicted due to its complete lack of an earlier era when contraction prevailed.

HOW GALAXIES ACQUIRED HALO STARS AS WELL

"Wait! What happened to the *'last 10 percent halo stars' that never got close enough together to form stellar clumps, as galaxies and globular clusters had done?"* someone shouted as loud as any fan in an arena.

"Precisely!" Kaidan replied. "As galaxies continued outbound with reversed dark energy's help, they captured still inbound halo stars as well. Galaxies still 'wear' them as sparkling cosmic 'tiaras.'

"Though these three stellar categories—globular clusters, elliptical galaxies and halo stars—all approached the cosmic center in that order, they were not the first forms of matter to arrive in that proximity. As I said earlier, half of the neutrinos and 45 percent of the electrons released by decaying neutrons flew away from the *inner* surface of the matter sphere. Converging at random angles across the vast inner space, some flew right through the cosmic center. Others simply crossed its general proximity. In either case, all such neutrinos and electrons ended up rushing out toward our three still in-rushing stellar communities.

"Keep in mind that every star, apart from a reunion with at least some of those long-lost electrons, must remain extremely ionized over eons of time. If ever stars would experience reduced ionization, some of those electrons passing through to that inner cosmic space would somehow have to make contact with them.

"I have more to say about electrons, galaxies and other cosmic phenomena; but first I want to ask you several questions.

KAIDAN'S EXULTANT REVIEW

"So—does everyone present in this Symposium understand," Kaidan summarized, "how it came about that globular clusters and halo stars, though formed apart from galaxies and even apart from each other, nonetheless ended up not only *orbiting* elliptical galaxies but more than that, orbiting galaxies *each with its own angular momentum?*"

A large number of Symposium attendees rose to their feet with an emphatic "Yes!" accompanied by cheers and clapping.

Arms outstretched, pacing along the edge of the dais, Kaidan pressed his enquiry further, asking "Tell me, does this new way of explaining the origin of the cosmos require charge parity to be violated?"

"No!" the audience murmured after a moment's thought.

"Does this cosmology require two billion universes to be uselessly formed and then uselessly annihilated so that this one universe may exist?" he asked again, this time with a fist pump.

"No!" the audience called back as one.

"Does this Sphere of Origin cosmology I describe require the extent continuum to hyper-inflate hundreds of times faster than the speed of light, only to brake immediately back down to pedestrian speeds?" he asked again.

"No!" the audience resounded with applause.

"Does it even provide a logically all-encompassing source for Cosmic Background Radiation?" Kaidan excitedly questioned further.

"Yes!" several participants shouted in growing response.

"Does it require 60 percent or more of its mass to consist of undetectable dark matter?" he queried again.

"No!" The audience roared aloud. By this time most attendees were standing and applauding.

"Does it negate the need for dark matter by offering *inbound* dark energy as a credible corollary to dark energy's current outbound phase?"

"It does indeed!" came the most audible response.

"Does it also offer to ease Doctors Tyson and Goldsmith's embarrassment over Big Bang Cosmology's failure to account for an equal mass of antimatter balancing all the matter that exists?"

"That, too!" came a resounding reply with chuckles.

"Does this new cosmology unveil a process that enables elliptical galaxies to sprout either lenticular disks or spiral arms, both of which become almost immediately enriched with heavy elements ready to solidify as planets and moons?"

"Yes!" participants bellowed with arms upraised.

"Does it assure that gravity did not have to work solo but was assisted by magnetism in forming stars and even planets and that there would be no need to undo a useless dark era?"

"Yes!" the audience resounded again.

Breathless and stunned as a phalanx of new perspectives competed for sites in his mind, James Engle bade goodbye to the last remnant of his personal, preferential resistance to Kaidan's incredibly *other* cosmology. *I have to accept this as the new reality*, James sighed internally. *My previous lectures and writings on subatomic physics and cosmology notwithstanding, so be it!*

Truth must triumph over fiction, no matter how well intentioned and seemingly conclusive that fiction may have been!

Justine texted her peers on the Loop: *This alien personality assuredly is more than just a masterful scientist. He is also a consummate psychologist and a gentleman to boot. Like Socrates with his students, he has been inviting us earth-blokes to experience firsthand, as it were, the joy of solving cosmic enigmas. He wants us to feel as if we are solving problem after problem almost from scratch, virtually on our own.*

Kent Madison, bowing his head in awe, prayed again—this time with utmost urgency—*God, my Lord, surely you must somehow be as central to Kaidan's steam-rolling cosmology as that inviolable 'cosmic center' that apparently is out there somewhere. Surely this amazing man from another world must know you or at least know about you, dear God. But if he truly does know you, how much longer can he keep teaching us about your creation without the slightest mention of your blessedly eternal existence?*

Not far away, atheist Charles Stein texted a fellow atheist: *Two hours of science and not a single breath wasted on theology or deity. How promising!*

CNN's Gregory Moore texted a CNN colleague seated elsewhere in the Symposium to say, *Wow—this is taxing my brain but it sure is worth the effort. The more I comprehend, the more I am filled with awe!*

Kaidan, meanwhile, drew a deep breath and sighed, knowing that his next statement would strike his worldwide audience as even more startling than what he had already unveiled. No matter. It, too, had to be made known.

Chapter Eight
Gravity's Unrecognized Complexity

In measured tones, Kaidan announced, "Mankind, I know all of you will find it almost impossible to accept what I am about to reveal. Even so, please be assured that what I'm about to say is verifiably true and easily proved. Since the birth of modern science here on Earth, you have been taught and you assuredly believe that gravity is a unidirectional force with *infinite reach*. It is now my obligation to inform you that gravity is a *bi-directional* force limited to a variety of *finite* reaches!

"As magnetism is finitely bipolar and dark energy is finitely bi-directional in terms of the matter cosmos contracting initially and then expanding, so also gravity is finitely bi-directional in terms of inward versus outward radial action. And that, my friends, is why the gravity waves Albert Einstein posited do not exist."

"Magnetism attracts *some* matter *toward* one pole while repelling the same matter *away* from an opposite pole. So also gravity attracts all matter toward one center of mass but only *within a given radius*. Simultaneously, gravity *repels* all matter within an outer radius *away* from that same center of mass!"

James's jaw dropped open in shock. So did Clyde Smith's and Homer Grassley's and William Stanfield's and Charles Stein's. Kent scanned the front and back of the Symposium venue and saw one television camera operator after another swivel his unit away from Kaidan. Far more crucial than filming the tall, serenely composed alien—for the moment, at least—was this rare opportunity to capture for posterity the mixture of stunned, shocked and utterly captivated expressions contorting the faces of scientists at the Symposium.

Grabbing her smartphone, Justine quickly texted everyone in the Loop: *SOS! SOS! Millions of doctors urgently needed for worldwide jaw repair!*

THE TWO DIRECTIONS OF GRAVITY

"Human experience thus far," Kaidan continued, "has all happened within the range of the Sun's radially inward gravity. I suggest we call it **esogravity** or an **esograv** field, since the prefix 'eso-' signifies 'inward.' Esogravity prevails from the center of the Sun out to a limit somewhere between the Sun and what Earth astronomers call the Oort cloud. Beyond that limit, the Sun's **exogravity** or **exograv** field—since the prefix 'exo-' signifies 'outward'—has always been there, *pushing* everything within its range radially *outward*. Beyond the Sun's exograv range, expelled matter keeps moving at a rate no longer affected by solar gravity at all. Beyond that radius, matter moves via momentum already instilled if not also by the gravity and/or magnetism of the galaxy.

GRAVITATIONAL 'LAYERING'

"Just as local bipolar magnetic fields occupy a finite space within Earth's magnetic field, which occupies a finite space within the Sun's magnetic field, so also gravitational fields are similarly *layered*," Kaidan continued. "The bi-directional gravity field encompassing each star or star cluster occupies its own finite space within the bi-directional gravity field of a galaxy. Likewise the bi-directional gravity field of each galaxy occupies a finite space within the bi-directional gravity field of galactic clusters.

"I'll have more to say about galactic esogravity and exogravity later, but for now, allow me simply to foretell that if any satellite NASA has launched ever reaches the Oort cloud," Kaidan promised, "exogravity will accelerate that satellite away from the Sun until the Sun's exograv limit is reached. The only question is, will that satellite's radio signals be strong enough to reveal to NASA that the satellite's recessional velocity is increasing?

HOW EXOGRAVITY PROTECTS US!

"People of Earth, why do tens of thousands of asteroids and comets collected over eons remain *stalled* far beyond Pluto in the Kuiper Belt and the even more distant Oort cloud? Why do all such potential intruders stay stalled there *'pro tem'* if not permanently?

"This happens because the Sun—in addition to its inner zone where esogravity attracts everything *Sun*-ward—also has a concentric outer sphere in which exogravity shields the inner solar system by slowing if not repelling everything else *outward*. Apart from the Sun's exograv shield, many more asteroids and comets would be roaming your inner solar system, potentially threatening life on Earth with deadly impacts.

"Borrowing terms from baseball, allow me to dub gravity's two zones 'the esograv *infield*' and 'the exograv *outfield*.'"

From within her hotel room, Becky Madison amusedly texted Kent: *I'm probably comprehending less of Kaidan's teaching than you are, but at least it's gratifying to hear an extraterrestrial recognize the significance of baseball!* ☺ *I L U !*

I thought you'd pick up on that if you were still tuned! Kent texted back, only to refocus immediately as Kaidan was saying: "Depending on the angle and velocity of their approach from interstellar space, some rocky interstellar nomads arrive with enough momentum to push through and join a star's esograv infield. Other wanderers are deflected away or even bounced straight back. Terra-astronomers, detecting their unaccountably retrograde motion, will of course assume that the gravity of a huge exterior planet or two must be overruling the Sun's inward draw."

Justine texted, *In all the annals of human thought, has there ever been a tsunami of insight more expansive than this one that has been buoying us up on its crest these past 2 hours and still continues to sweep us onward to who knows what?*

"Yet on the positive side," Kaidan continued, "it is also true that every star that has an esograv/exograv infield and outfield all to itself also has a far better potential to host its own planetary system. Stars that enjoy that special privilege are stars like your Sun and mine, stars which—like the halo stars mentioned earlier—

enjoy relative isolation from other stars whether in the exterior of an elliptical galaxy or in a galactic disk or arm.

"Conversely, those myriad stars that linked together as globular clusters or elliptical galaxies during dark energy's early inbound phase are obligated to share their esograv infields and their exograv outfields in common. For reasons already explained, those stars do not produce the heavy elements needed to make planets; hence they have no planets. Planets in that context would have difficulty staying in orbit around just one star! Such planets would end up switching orbits from one star to the next and plunge eventually into one of the nearest stars and be consumed.

HOW THE 'GOLDEN MEAN' RELATES TO GRAVITY

"Curiously, the golden mean—**1.618034**—divided by itself twice equals itself minus one—**0.618034**—whereas the golden mean *squared* equals itself *plus* one—**2.618034**. It is also the basis of the so-called Fibonacci series, a ratio that shows up repeatedly in the cosmos. In relation to gravity, the golden mean dictates the ratio of the radius of a star's esograv infield to the radius of the same star's exograv outfield. So if the radius of your Sun's esograv infield happens to be **26.18034** astronomical units—an astronomical unit (AU) being the distance from the Sun to Earth— the radius of the Sun's exograv outfield will add another **16.18034 AUs**. In that case, the Sun's exograv outfield will extend no further than **42.36068 AUs** from the Sun.

HOW GALAXIES ALSO MANIFEST EXOGRAVITY

"As terra-astronomers are aware, many stars in the outer arms of spiral galaxies manifest velocities too rapid and vectors too odd to be explained in terms of Newtonian gravity, which affects stars *inwardly* in relation to galactic nuclei. Terra-theorists credit the odd motion of such stars to dark matter gravity, as if dark matter, after coalescing galaxies inwardly, could leap to their exteriors and tries to reverse part of what it coalesced by drawing a galaxy's outermost stars *away*!

"Terra-science self-contradicts again by positing dark matter gravity as pulling ordinary matter together while leaving itself conveniently dispersed. These hypothetical masses of dark matter, seemingly, are so content to 'hang out' around ordinary-matter galaxies that they never get around to coalescing *themselves* as dark matter galaxies. They also posit ordinary gravity as strong enough to coalesce 'black holes' in ordinary matter. Why then doesn't dark matter gravity, posited as ever so much stronger, coalesce 'dark matter black holes'?

"Actually, a *few* terra-cosmologists," Kaidan admitted, "can't help themselves; they simply must reject the dark matter hypothesis. One 2015 issue of *Discover* magazine, for example, features an article boldly titled, 'Dark Matter Deniers.' The author, Steve Nadis, recounts that more than thirty years ago, Israeli theoretical physicist Mordehai Milgrom, convinced that 'dark matter' simply does not exist, brought forth an alternate theory known as MOND, short for *Modified Newtonian Dynamics*.

"According to Milgrom, wherever Newtonian gravity's ability to attract matter falls below a threshold of ten to the minus ten $[10^{-10}]$ meters per second, an alternate version of gravity—designated the MONDrian kind—replaces classical Newtonian gravity. From that radius outward, MONDrian gravity keeps growing stronger to an apparently unspecified maximum limit at an unspecified maximum radius.

"Gravity at Milgrom's transitional threshold of maximum weakness, Nadis says, is 100 billion times weaker than gravity at the surface of the Earth.

"Voilà! Milgrom and collaborator Stacy McCaugh of Case Western Reserve University in Cleveland, Ohio, all unwitting, are standing within inches of discovering exogravity. All they need is to specify MONDrian gravity as gravity in reverse pushing matter out to a radius linked to inward gravity's radius by a golden-mean-related ratio. That, along with specifying inward and outward gravity as able to switch places, would be fully accurate.

"Milgrom and McCaugh readily find evident Newtonian/ MONDrian transition points in low luminosity dwarf galaxies. Finding that transition point in very bright, very massive and often clustered galaxies is proving more difficult. All the while, both researchers have had to endure a trial of professional criticism.[16]

"So, then, the unique vectors common to these outlying spiral arm stars do not in any way affirm the existence of dark matter. Magnetically expelled long ago with enough force to break free from a parent galaxy's esograv infield, all such stars—far from being pulled out by dark matter—are actually being *pushed* out and away by exogravity in the same galaxy's 'outfield.'

"Now—along with evidence that exogravity encompasses individual *stars*, another most curious feature of many galaxies provides visible proof that exogravity exists. Here is photographic evidence that exogravity reigns in galactic outfields as surely as esogravity dominates galactic infields," Kaidan promised.

THE SPECIAL CASE OF *BARRED* SPIRAL GALAXIES

Kaidan, clicking his remote control again, exhibited a series of photographs, one on each screen, featuring seven galaxies belonging to a category dubbed by astrophysicists as 'barred spirals.' [NGC 1300—'C' in the photo section—is an example.]

Kaidan continued: "The unusual shape of barred spiral galaxies cannot be explained in terms of esogravity alone. Whereas spiral arms in many galaxies begin arcing relatively close to the expelling nucleus, millions more feature spiral arms that arc instead from the *ends of a straight bar* which, in ways unknown to Isaac Newton, extend far out on opposite sides of galactic nuclei.

"Dr. Engle, while describing galactic-strength magnetic pole reversals ejecting stars consecutively from opposite sides of elliptical galaxies, posed two scenarios for us. First, he correctly premised that stars hurled out *less forcefully* lag behind the spin of an ejecting galaxy while remaining close enough to its girth to form an attached disk. The expelling nucleus plus the disk thus become what astronomers label as a 'lenticular' galaxy.

"Second, stars jettisoned at greater velocities begin lagging at greater distances from the nucleus. Such stars leave an arced gap widening between themselves and the ejecting galaxy. Ultimately, though, as the expelling galaxy's esogravity slows their outbound velocity, all expelled stars begin arcing around as 'spiral arms.'

"The nuclei of *barred* spiral galaxies, conversely, expel stars so forcefully that the rotational lag characteristic of spiral arms is delayed until the stars expelled form two straight bars projecting from magnetic poles on opposite sides of expelling nuclei. Only when these two bars are complete do expelled stars begin lagging behind the *ends* of each bar! With so many stars forming the straight bars themselves, fewer stars are left for the spiral arms that lag from the ends of the two straight bars.

"Dr. Engle, I invite you to crown your two earlier insights by explaining why some galaxies feature these odd bars."

Here we go again, Justine texted the Loop. *Arkona's Socrates at his best. Is James ready with a third ingenious reply?*

James rose slowly to his feet, shaking his head in awe. Taking a hand mic, he admitted, "I can hardly believe this! Here I am, about to affirm something I would have dismissed, only an hour ago, as preposterous. But now—Yes, please let me try!"

JAMES ENGLE'S THIRD INSIGHT

All eyes were fixed on James as he commenced his explanation. "Ladies and Gentlemen, and Kaidan (of course), we have no choice but to posit galactic-strength magnetic expulsions several magnitudes more powerful than those I described earlier. Stars jettisoned first from one pole and then from the other by these very powerful magnetic reversals achieve what less forceful expulsions could not accomplish. The stars they expel transit the expelling galaxy's esograv infield so swiftly that they enter the same galaxy's exograv outfield before any significant lag occurs relative to the rotation of the expelling galaxy!

"Whatever momentum outbound stars lose while overcoming esogravity's inward draw is now regained, even amplified, as exogravity restores their original outbound velocity. That must be why, despite the time elapsed, the bars remain straight while distance from the nucleus is increasing. I see now, ever so clearly, that regular spiral arms lag the way they do because they exist exclusively within what Kaidan describes as a galaxy's 'esograv *infield*.' I also see that barred spiral galaxies prove that galaxies also have *exograv outfields*! As far as I am concerned, Kaidan, barred spiral galaxies confirm that exo-gravity does indeed exist." James sat down, awaiting a reply from Kaidan.

"I commend you, Dr. Engle," Kaidan responded, adding, "Your third response is equally as apt as your first two. And now, putting the matter of lenticular disks, spiral arms and even barred spiral arms behind us, I invite all of you to join me as we tackle another intriguing question related to galaxies.

WHY FEW GALAXIES COLLIDED
IN THE GREAT CONFLUENCE

"Has anyone wondered why relatively few galaxies collided forcefully enough to merge in the Great Cosmic Confluence?" Kaidan asked.

"Yes! I did wonder about that!" Clyde Smith began even before an aide handed him a mic. "But now I surmise that galaxies, as cosmic behemoths, entered the Great Cosmic Confluence 'wearing' exograv shields like outer garments. That must explain why relatively few galaxies collided forcefully enough to merge."

"You, too, are spot-on correct, Clyde," Kaidan said. "And I hope now that everyone understands why—although some galaxies were destined to collide and even merge—exogravity enabled an enormous majority of galaxies to rebound away from each other like balls on a billiards table. And that rebounding is also what altered their trajectories significantly enough to result in *clusters* of galaxies becoming subject to that ultimate layer of esogravity: the kind with the longest reach!"

Symposium attendees rose to their feet again with further applause. *Already this articulate alien has taken all of us and perhaps much of mankind*, William Stanfield texted to everyone on the Loop, *so far beyond what any of us knew or ever expected to know. What on earth could he possibly come up with next?*

"Thank you," Kaidan said, acknowledging the ovation and motioning for all to be seated. "I am relieved to find that you, and hopefully many others worldwide, accept the evidence that gravity is just as bi-directional as magnetism is bipolar. Returning now to the topic of exogravity in *stars*, I suspect all of you will be just as surprised by what I am about to declare: namely, that bi-directional gravity is also just as *reversible* as is bipolar magnetism!

"Just as magnetic fields reverse their polarity under certain conditions, so also the law of gravity, under certain conditions, requires a star's esograv infield and its exograv outfield to switch places instantly with awesome results. This grand event occurs rather commonly in stars but almost never in galaxies.

"Earlier I spoke of stars 'exploding' as supernovae. Let me clarify: what we see as *explosions* are actually something else.

HOW CAN STARS EXPLODE AS NOVAE
YET KEEP ON SHINING AFTERWARD?

"When a bomb explodes, no one expects to find that bomb slightly smaller in size but still intact and getting ready to explode again. Yet when stars explode, they do so in such a way that *heavy elements* are expelled while light gases stay behind to reconstitute the star with slightly less mass ready for *still more* explosions! How can this happen? Some stars, after several explosions, eventually do expire as brown dwarfs; but what about until then?

"Look at **V838 Monocerotis**. [See 'E' in photo section.] The star has expelled masses of opaque heavy elements without destroying itself in the process. Look also at the **Cat's Eye Nebula**. [See 'F' in photo section.] The central star has launched successive masses of heavier elements while still retaining enough hydrogen and helium to keep shining as if it had never exploded. It even seems ready to fuse still more heavy elements for future explosions! *How can mindless explosions sophisticatedly sort out what to expel and what to retain? There is only one logical answer.*

VIA GRAVITY REVERSALS, STARS EJECT HEAVY
ELEMENTS WHILE RETAINING THEIR MAIN MASS

"What precipitates a gravity reversal in and around a star?" Kaidan asked. "Why would a star's exograv outfield suddenly switch places with a star's esograv infield?

"I reply: just as magnetic fields reverse so as to keep one pole from becoming critically overloaded relative to the other, so also gravity just as readily reverses its inner and outer fields so as *to prevent esogravity from exceeding a certain critical pressure on the core of a star*. Terra-astronomers, noting a maximum mass beyond which white dwarf stars explode as supernovae, designate that mass as the Chandrasekhar Limit. Still, they fail to credit that limit as triggering actual gravity reversals. Nor do they extrapolate mass limits triggering the same effect in other kinds of stars.

"Suffice it to say, when gravity switches its inner and outer fields, both parts of the overall field carry their above-mentioned golden-mean-based radial ratios with them to their new locations.

"Primarily, gravity reversals alter stars in one of three ways. Depending on a star's mass and how great a mass of middle-weight elements it has accumulated, a reversed-gravity star becomes either *a **nova** or a **supernova***. Failing that, it becomes either a **hollow star** or a **variable one**.

"All stars had to form initially," Kaidan recalled, "from coalesced plasmas of the very lightest elements—hydrogen and helium with traces of deuterium, tritium and lithium. As I explained earlier, GSISC—gravity sharing in stellar community—tends to prevent stars in globular clusters and elliptical galaxies from making middle-mass elements (let alone *heavy* elements). Hence gravity reversals occur in halo stars and in the spiral arm and barred spiral arm stars that encircle galactic nuclei. That is where, over time, stars fuse light-mass nuclei to form **middle-mass elements**: neon, argon, boron, sodium, chlorine, carbon, oxygen and nitrogen, to name several. It takes something more than ordinary 'gravity pressure,' however, for stars to fuse the heaviest elements in the periodic table—iron, silver, lead, gold, etc.

TRULY HEAVY ELEMENTS, AT LAST!

"Eventually, the gravity pressure of an increasing mass of middle-weight elements pressing down on the cores of these select stellar categories triggers a crisis. Adding middle-mass elements to a star's always-present light elements gradually raises gravity's pressure on the core of a star up to gravity's legal limit. Yes, just as *light* has a maximum velocity, gravity has a maximum pressure. Rather than exceed its pressure limit, *gravity reverses*!

"In other words, the force named earlier as **exogravity** instantly replaces the more familiar **esogravity** at the very core of a star. Ergo the inner mass of the star, starting at its core, surges very forcefully *outward*. This happens before the outer mass of the star has had time to lose *the inbound momentum* esogravity was imparting to it until that moment! Esogravity is no longer there but the momentum it generated is still crucially pressing stellar matter *inward*. Can anyone guess what happens?"

Physicist Homer Grassley leaped to his feet. "Kaidan, with exogravity suddenly opposing the momentum esogravity had imparted to inbound matter, surely the pressure generated when the switch occurs becomes another temporary means of fusing innumerable tons of middle-weight elements into *heavy* elements!

"Surely also much of the **middle-weight elements a star has amassed will be fused almost instantly into a lode of heavy elements**! These heavy elements will range from *tin, zinc, silicon, manganese, aluminum, iron, copper, silver and lead* to *gold, platinum, uranium and plutonium*, among others.

"So! Heavy elements get to form coincidentally while gravity guards its legality. How clever!" Homer interjected and sat down grinning.

"You are exactly correct!" Kaidan replied. "As quickly as this new mass of heavy elements forms, exogravity gets to hurl all of it out toward the interface where internal exogravity and external esogravity now oppose each other face to face! Once this transfer of venues is complete, a further phase enables this already complete heavy element production to be followed by a phenomenal heavy element expulsion, as follows:

THE NOVA AND SUPERNOVA OPTIONS

"When a critical mass of medium-weight elements triggers a gravity reversal in a star, the star expands explosively as described. Masses of light and medium-mass elements plus all of the *at-that-very-moment-forming* heavy elements explode out into the surrounding vacuum, causing the star's brightness to flare.

"Initially, all the expelled light, medium and brand new heavy elements vacate the center of the star at the same velocity. Why so? As surely as esogravity makes a cannonball and a peanut fall at the same rate in a vacuum, so also exogravity expels light, medium and heavy elements from the center of an exploding star at equal rates. That said, exogravity, in the process, imparts much more momentum to the star's heavy and medium-mass elements than it does to the star's lighter components.

"That fact becomes crucially significant when that ballooning mix of varied elements meets a winnowing barrier. I refer to the spherical interface where exogravity and esogravity are pressing hard against each other. All of the star's lightweight hydrogen and helium—having less momentum—is now *stalled almost instantly* by the esograv barrier's retarding effect. As for middle-mass and heavy elements, if the gravity reversal of an exploding star imparted enough momentum, those elements alone break through the esograv barrier, thus filling the exploded star's outfield with a rich mix of heavier elements. When that happens, the result is either a nova or a supernova, depending upon the force of the reversal and the quantity of heavy elements expelled.

"With all of the star's hydrogen and helium winnowed and retained and all of the star's heavier elements expelled as a nebula, **gravity is no longer in crisis mode**, so eso- and exo-gravity pop back to their standard locations! Accordingly, all of the hydrogen and helium retained in the stellar infield collapse back in to re-form the star with slightly less mass. Likewise, with gravity's original reversal reversed, all of the star's successfully expelled middle- and heavy-mass elements get a powerful outbound boost, now that exogravity is back in its external domain. However, these expelled heavy elements do not form new stars, as terra-scientists contend. Heavy elements are much more apt to form planets and moons that—dispersed galaxy-wide by birthing nebulae—are captured later by other stars to form solar systems. More about that later.

"Conversely, if most of the star's middle- and heavy-mass elements *lack the momentum needed for a complete breakout*, they too are retained at the interface where the star's two forms of gravity are still pushing against each other. Thus the continuing force of heavy elements pressing, not against a tiny core but against both sides of a vast spherical surface, maintains the crisis that led to a gravity reversal in the first place. Everything in that situation, light elements included, instead of forming an expanding nebula, leads to option number 2 as follows.

THE HOLLOW STAR PHENOMENON

"With exogravity pressing *out* from the inside and esogravity pulling in from the outside, a star's light elements and any medium-mass elements that fail to escape become fixed in the shape of a huge sphere that is *hollow* except for the energy trapped within! As magnetic reversals keep expelling heavy elements from the sphere's exterior, the need for reversed gravity diminishes until the reversal ends. When esogravity and exogravity pop back to their preferred places, the hollow star collapses to become once again a smaller fiery ball with greatly diminished luminosity.

"Some hollow stars—Antares and Betelgeuse are nearby examples—are so enormous that the orbits of not only Mercury and Venus but even of Earth and Mars could fit inside them! According to modern astrophysics, stars as enormous as these ought to collapse as black holes."

Despite his shock at the notion of gravity being bi-directionally reversible and a star being hollow, James had to admit that Kaidan was solving a mystery that had long troubled him. Kaidan was right. According to astrophysics, if stars as large as Betelgeuse and Antares are filled with mass throughout their entire volume, each star's gravity ought to be strong enough to collapse it down to the size of a black hole! Kaidan was simply explaining how stars could be that massive yet still keep shining as stars.

"Can hollow stars sustain enough pressure on their hydrogen balloon to keep fusing it to make helium?" Kaidan asked. "The answer is, the convergent pressure of esogravity opposing exogravity linked with the pressure of intense radiation trapped inside such stars proves minimally adequate.

"Apart from the winnowing effect of an exterior esograv barrier encompassing a star that has exploded due to gravity reversal, every atom of its hydrogen and helium would simply join all the medium and heavy elements in a mass exodus. Conserved outbound momentum in that event would leave nothing to reconstitute the exploded star so as to continue shining as usual at the same site where the nova or supernova occurred.

"Frankly, terra-astronomers have long been remiss by failing to explain why conservation of momentum fails to keep most of an exploding star's hydrogen and helium from expanding in concert with all those heavy elements. Every supernova that still has a reconstituted star at its center after expelling its heavier elements is the boldest possible evidence that a gravity reversal happened and then reversed again. Face it! There is no other way to explain this amazing phenomenon.

THE VARIABLE STAR OPTION

"Just as magnetic fields can reverse their two polarities *repeatedly*, so also gravity fields can reverse their two positions repeatedly. That is exactly what causes some stars to shine with a brightness that fluctuates. They are known as **'variable stars.'**

"If magnetic field reversals on the exterior surface of a hollow star expel enough ionized heavy elements almost as soon as a hollow star forms, the gravity reversal *reverses*, whereupon esogravity pulls the entire remaining mass of the star inward with enormous force. The pressure ensuing at the star's core fuses a new mass of heavy elements instantly. The renewed presence of heavy elements triggers another reversal followed by another collapse. Gravity reversals keep recurring. A 'variable star' ensues.

"Now let me explain what happens when significant masses of medium and heavy elements birthed by the explosion of a star actually break through the esograv barriers around such stars to form very large nebulae. Terra-cosmologists persistently claim that such nebulae become star-birthing 'nurseries.' However, stars coalesce from *light* elements suited to nuclear fusion, not from opaque heavy elements which are extremely averse to serving as fuel for fusion in the cores of stars. As thousands of photos of nebulae reveal, most nebulae consist primarily of darkly opaque clouds consisting of kinds of matter much too heavy for stars to burn as fuel. Nowhere do we see the flat disks of gas in which terra-scientists claim a star is sure to form at the center with orbiting planets already coalescing at proper distances from the star.

"Dr. Raman Prinja, whom I cited earlier," Kaidan commented, "states that:

> "...astronomers have long suspected that stars would be surrounded by leftover gas and dust swirling in a pancake-shaped disc....Known as 'proto-planetary discs,' they are thought to be composed of 99 percent gas and 1 percent dust particles, although even this tiny amount of dust makes the discs opaque and difficult to view and image.[17]

"Next, Dr. Prinja claims that infrared instruments do indeed detect hidden discs embedded in nebulae. Still, the image he provides on pages 64 and 65 of his book is only a 'computer-generated simulation.'[18] If millions of new stars were forming in pancake-shaped disks located just a few thousand light years from Earth, surely at least a few such 'disks' would have popped up in open space where they could be photographed in visible light.

"One suspects there is much more than just 1 percent of heavy element 'dust' in the gaseous nebulae terra-astronomers credit as star-forming nurseries. In fact, the percentage of heavy elements is such that there is not enough hydrogen and helium in such nebulae to form stars at all! Planets and moons, however, find just what they need to form in abundance!

"If enough hydrogen was available to form second-generation stars in such nebulae, there could not also be enough hydrogen to reform the central star itself at the cores of such nebulae. Indeed, the predominance of opaque heavier matter in all such nebulae indicates they are actually birthing planets and moons much more than new stars. I will now explain how that happens."

Chapter Nine
How Solar Systems Form

Drawing another deep breath, Kaidan continued: "As I have already stated, astronomy on my home planet differs from terra-astronomy as to how solar systems form. Scientists here, modeling mainly from this solar system, posit as follows:

(1) Part of a cloud of supernova debris, despite the turbulent expansion of the supernova, somehow flattens like a pancake spinning on a central axis. Also like a pancake, its mass is thick at the center, thin at the edges.

(2) The 'pancake' allots its light, medium and heavy elements to distinct regions. Oddly enough, ultra-light gases—hydrogen and helium—tend to coalesce *centrally*, forming a later-generation star with minimal traces of medium to heavy elements in its mass.

(3) Heavier gases coalesce much further out, where they tend to orbit contiguously as gas giant planets.

(4) Rocky planets—except for those orbiting gas giants as moons—also appear to enjoy each other's company. They coalesce and may orbit contiguously *between* the new second-generation star and the gas giants.

(5) Earth scientists posit gravity as the prime planet-coalescing agent. Explaining the origin of the cosmos via Big Bang Cosmology embeds a bias. If indeed the cosmos began with no ionization hence no magnetism, as the Big Bang demands, gravity has to be the sole star-coalescing factor.

Magnetism is absent. That same bias, once instilled, leads one to overlook magnetism's role in the subsequent formation of planetary systems.

WHY THEN DO WE SEE, NOT 'PANCAKES' BUT ONLY *'PILLARS'* OF CREATION?

"If indeed solar systems begin as pancake-shaped disks spinning amid supernova debris, photographs of supernova-generated nebulae ought to present at least a few thicker-in-the-middle disks comprised mainly of hydrogen and helium. Yet photos of pancake-shaped proto-solar systems are conspicuously *absent* in reams of photographs of supernova nebulae. Instead, photos of supernova-generated nebulae feature what astronomers commonly describe as 'pillars of creation,' i.e., pillars in which new *stars* are forming, stars supposedly replete with planets.

"According to terra-theory, shouldn't we be seeing *pancakes* rather than *pillars* of creation?

"Yet even the word 'pillars' is a misnomer since it implies straight columns. What we see instead are crooked *fingers*, not of hydrogen and helium but of very opaque hence heavier matter bending abruptly in ways that gravity alone cannot explain. [See, for example, 'G' and 'H' in the photo section.] Virtually all of these conspicuous 'fingers' bend at angles or even turn a corner here and there. Surely such amazing mobility would twist pancake-shaped planetary disks all out of shape, would it not?

"As explained earlier, once heavy elements in a reversed-gravity supernova surge past the interface where exogravity meets esogravity, gravity promptly un-reverses. Thus exogravity, restored to its *external* zone, forcefully accelerates everything within its reach on outbound trajectories. Why then, seeing that gravity acts radially, do these outbound trajectories begin turning odd corners en route? Why doesn't everything just keep moving on straight lines?

"The answer is, of course, that high levels of ionization in the expelled masses trigger magnetic field reversals. As for MFRs, they are not all that concerned about conforming strictly to radii. So, as in the very early cosmos, imbalanced magnetic fields, by reversing their poles, begin redirecting, not hydrogen and helium this time, but heavy elements destined to form various kinds of planets, moons, comets and asteroids by the time they fully exit from the nebulae where they form.

"Simply put, if magnetic fields are imbalanced enough to reverse, it is because the matter they expel is still ionized. Ergo new magnetic fields form, only to reverse again and again except that each subsequent reversal tends to expel matter in rather *different directions!* That is why photos of various nebula exhibit masses of expelled opaque planet-forming material forming 'fingers' that keep bending in different directions, even turning corners [as in photo 'H'].

"The end result is that planets, moons and comets begin dispersing across interstellar space, leaving far behind the supernova debris clouds that spawned them. Just as certain plants release *spores* into the wind, supernovae spread planets, moons and comets galaxy-wide!

"Please remember: stars form mainly from *light* elements suitable for nuclear fusion. Rarely do stars form amid the opaque, already-fused heavy elements we see in supernova nebulae. Elements that are already heavy are extremely resistant to further fusion. Besides, the sheer *opacity* of enormous quantities of heavy elements in such stars would serve only to *blockade* the photons released by fusion in their cores. With photons blockaded in their cores, any such stars, if they could exist at all, would simply explode rather than shine for billions of years.

"Along with the above comments, I must now explain something else that terra-science leaves unexplained.

OTHER INCONSISTENCIES

"Consider Earth's solar system: if the Sun and all its planets and moons coalesced from one 'solar disk,' surely that disk would have reached a state of *chemical homogeneity* long before the Sun and everything orbiting around it coalesced. Yet your eight planets plus all the moons and comets in this system are by no means chemically homogeneous! Mercury, Venus, Earth, Mars, the gas giants and many of the various moons and comets are remarkably diverse as to the chemicals they exhibit. Obviously each planet, moon, and comet bears the chemical signature of something other than whatever gave existence to the Sun.

"Surely any such disk would also have rendered itself *homogeneously ionized* long before the Sun and all its planets and moons had time to form. Surely planets and moons formed out in the suburbs of this solar system ought to be as homogeneously ionized as is the Sun at the hub. How then do we explain why all the planets, moons and comets in this, your own solar system, manifest extremely low levels of ionization compared to the Sun?

"Every first-generation star had to coalesce from little more than highly ionized hydrogen and helium. Medium and heavyweight elements needed to form planets, moons and comets were absent. How then can it be that many chemically simple, highly ionized first-generation stars have chemically complex, minimally ionized planets, moons and comets orbiting around them?

"This extreme contrast between the chemical simplicity and high ionization of a typical star versus the chemical complexity and reduced ionization of planetoids orbiting around them testifies that the latter had to form elsewhere and be added to the stars later."

With another click of his remote control, Kaidan displayed his next message.

WHY THEN DO PLANETS EXPELLED FROM SUPERNOVAE BECOME MUCH LESS IONIZED WHILE VOYAGING TO BE CAPTURED BY OTHER STARS?

"There can be no doubt that the unique mix of chemicals found in any planet, moon or comet reflects the unique chemical makeup of whichever distant supernova spawned it. So how are we to explain why planetoids formed from highly ionized heavy elements have lost most of their ionization by the time they are captured by other stars to form solar systems?

"From our earlier discussion, do you recall what happened to 90 percent of the electrons released by neutron decay in the early minutes of the cosmos?" Kaidan queried.

Homer Grassley requested a hand mic and replied. "I believe we concluded that only about 10 percent of all the electrons released were captured by protons on the matter sphere. We also deduced that half of the remainder sped away irrecoverably *outside* the matter sphere. The other 45 percent, I presume, are still roaming this matter sphere's vast interior. These are thus the only electrons available to de-ionize any protons they happen to meet in interstellar space."

HOW LONG-LOST INNER-SPACE ELECTRONS SERVED THEIR PURPOSE AT LAST!

"Correct, Mr. Grassley!" Kaidan enjoined. "There can be no doubt: every planet, moon or comet began its interstellar journey just as highly ionized as the nebula that birthed it. Yet every planet, moon and comet also becomes enormously less ionized than whichever star eventually captures it gravitationally.

"This observation validates not only that every planet orbiting your Sun had to be expelled by a gravity reversal working in tandem with MFRs in a distant supernova but also that each such orb had to roam freely in Dr. Grassley's *electron-rich interstellar space* long enough to lose most of its ionization before being naturalized within your Sun's esograv domain. Only by voyaging for an eon or two amid electrons in interstellar space could planets, moons, and comets become as de-ionized as they are found to be.

"Ionization levels diminish gradually as more and more interstellar electrons, estranged from protons since the genesis of the cosmos, are drawn magnetically and gravitationally toward proto-planets and/or moons passing by like ships in the night.

"Because electrons take much longer to penetrate the enormous mass of 'gas giant' planets, the latter commonly remain more ionized than do smaller worlds. Shifting inward from crust to core, changing ions to atoms as they progress, interstellar electrons render *rocky planets* much less ionized hence *potentially amenable to forms of life*. Rocky planets with just enough in-core ionization to sustain magnetic shields that counter harmful radiation can be classified as 'bio-fit,' other factors permitting.

"Extreme ionization, by the way, is hostile to life. Try to imagine static electricity in your hair, in your clothing and especially in your flesh and bones and blood amplified by several thousand magnitudes!

"Granted, then—stars formed *first* with the possibility that planetoids cast in all directions by magnetically active novae and supernovae will arrive with sufficient momenta to do what?" Kaidan asked.

"With sufficient momenta to penetrate a recipient star's exograv barrier and gain access to its esograv infield!" Homer Grassley volunteered again.

"Exactly!" Kaidan acknowledged.

"Why, then," James Engle asked, "does the Sun's exograv barrier, as Homer describes it, favor admitting planetoids close to the Sun's equatorial plane—the ecliptic—rather than from any and all directions?"

"Wisely asked!" Kaidan replied. "Mainly, the flattening of the Sun's magnetic lines of force close above and close below the ecliptic renders the Sun's exograv outfield more penetrable close to the ecliptic. As for planetoids that arrive high above or far below the ecliptic, if they still retain a fair degree of ionization, either the Sun's positive pole will repel them or the Sun's negative pole will draw them directly into the Sun. There is also another factor; namely, the gravity of two or three or more already-in-place gas giants helps to pull higher-flying later-arriving orbs down or lift lower dipping later-arriving orbs up toward the ecliptic over time.

"What I am saying here contrasts sharply with captions I find under photos of nebulae in science magazines, books and on the Internet. Most captions credit supernova nebulae as birthing *stars*. Captions also consistently credit *gravity* as the sole coalescing agent for 'next-generation stars.' But gravity cannot accelerate dark knots of matter faster than the expansion rate of the nebula itself! Nor can gravity explain why so many knots of matter *keep changing direction*!

"In almost every photo of a nebula, dozens if not hundreds of dark, dusty, non-luminescent knots of matter are vectored—not just radially outward, as one would expect after a customary explosion, *but at random angles relative to the supernova core!*

"Not only so, but also many of these apparently solid or semi-solid knots of matter are trailed by streams of dusty gas reminiscent of trails of smoke left by moving torches. Odder still, zigzags in the dusty gas trails reveal that the objects they trail have been *changing their course* occasionally so as to turn corners again and again on their generally outbound trajectories.

"The outward momentum instilled by a supernova blast cannot by itself explain why these curious objects, once formed, keep repeatedly and randomly gaining new momentum and altering their directions. Terra-science, for its part, has barely even bothered to notice this eye-catching phenomenon, let alone try to explain it. Allow me to display the following examples."

One after another, full-color photos of nebulae appeared on the seven-screen display, accompanied by Kaidan's comments.

THE CAT'S EYE NEBULA

"As I mentioned earlier, the Cat's Eye Nebula features a series of overlapping translucent spheres of exploded gas from which two knots of heavy matter have been ejected into space in opposite directions. [See 'F' in the photo section] Note also that each ejected knot of matter leaves a curiously multi-angled trail of dusty gas behind it. Arko-cosmology attributes this series of 'corners' in the two gas trails to successive random magnetic field reversals, both of which, over time, have been redirecting the two magnetically impelled knots of denser matter.

"Compare the size of the knot at the end of each gas trail with the diameter of the central star itself," Kaidan reasoned, "and we find that neither knot has sufficient mass to form a new star! Just as obviously, each knot does have enough heavy matter for magnetism abetted by gravity to coalesce it as a *planet*.

"Ladies and gentlemen, we are seeing two gravitationally coalesced but also magnetically ejected *planets* leaving the Cat's Eye Nebula on two separate interstellar journeys. Eventually, the electrons these still highly-ionized nodes collect while crossing interstellar space will reduce their ionization to such a degree that magnetic reversals will eventually cease redirecting their trajectories. From that point on, momentum alone will vector them toward other stars.

"Ages later, after crossing interstellar space via momentum alone, either one or perhaps both planets ejected from the Cat's Eye may at last be captured by the gravity of other stars. One wanderer may be added to an existing solar system. Another may become the first member of an entirely new system.

"Bon voyage, questing travelers!" Kaidan called.

James felt stunned to realize how many times he had glanced at photos of the Cat's Eye Nebula without paying the slightest attention to that obvious series of 'corners' in the gas trails left by both faster-moving knots of matter above and below the star. How could he repeatedly miss something he now saw as patently obvious? Kaidan, meanwhile, was saying:

"A headline in a magazine referencing the Carina Nebula [see 'G' in the photo section] reads: *'Unsolved Mystery: What Processes Operate Deep Within Nebulae Where Stars Are Born?'*[19]

"Actually there is no mystery at all! Dozens of corner-turning heavy matter nodes are leaving zigzag trails around the edges of the Carina Nebula. This shows that MFRs are in the process of coalescing not stars but rather a *huge* number of planets and similar heavy-elements entities.

"Preferring Big Bang Cosmology to the 'double bubble' system has disadvantaged terra-scientists from start to finish. First, Big Bang Cosmology forces them to justify star formation via gravity with zero help from magnetism's MFRs. True to that pattern, they also struggle to explain how planets form, again with zero help from magnetism. At least terra-scientists are consistent.

"Now, please watch the screens carefully as I display photo after photo of dozens of novae and supernovae," Kaidan instructed, adding, "Note how many conical, finger-shaped tubes of opaque matter project beyond the main mass of each nebula.

"Note that each and every one of these tubes has somehow been invested with a fresh, linear momentum that enables it to leave the remainder of the nebula in its angular wake. These are proto-worlds or smaller facsimiles of the same, many of which are destined—after age-long journeys across de-ionizing interstellar space—to be captured by stars that are either devoid of planets or have room for more."

Tiny white arrows in the photos on all seven screens directed viewer attention to make Kaidan's point very clear.

"Let me assure you," Kaidan continued, "that for every proto-planet large enough to be seen from Earth, thousands more too small to be detected are also in flight. Some are vectored toward virtually every star in the arms of every spiral galaxy."

The last nebula in that final series Kaidan displayed was part of what astronomers call The Monkey Head.

THE MONKEY HEAD, NGC 2174 [see photo 'H']

Highlighting dozens of jets of opaque matter protruding from the Monkey Head Nebula, Kaidan asked, "I repeat: which force is uniquely accelerating each of these dark jets such that they leave the nebula that birthed them far behind? Also, which force simultaneously enables each jet to keep altering its direction? Motions such as these are not due to standard gravity. Magnetism is the only additional force and magnetic field reversals are the only feature of magnetism that suffices to explain what we see.

"Large jets consisting mainly of hydrogen and helium could indeed coalesce as stars, but such jets would be much less opaque than these, inasmuch as hydrogen and helium are relatively transparent gases. These jets consist primarily of the heavy matter needed to form iron and silica-cored planets, moons and comets.

"If we Arkonans, along with other citizens of the 24-planet Federation, find a star with a rocky planet that is *almost* ready to support life, we take pleasure in 'mining' that star's exterior Kuiper Belt for small orbs laden with elements that a candidate planet needs in order to qualify as bio-fit. Finding such orbs, we maneuver them via our space vehicles so that the star's esogravity can pull them in as comets. With further course corrections, the orbs we select eventually impact the candidate planet, adding water and the makings for an atmosphere."

Brent saw several scientists gaping at Kaidan in awe. How awesome that finite beings with finite technology could 'bio-fit' barren rocky planets enough to support eco-systems. Homer texted on the Loop, asking, *Could they or we perhaps bio-fit Mars?*

"To summarize," Kaidan continued, "if your Sun, these eight planets and all these moons had accreted from one disk, the element make-up and ionization levels of this entire system would match what is characteristic of the Sun. Rather, planets and moons in this and every other solar system reveal the chemistry of whichever far-away supernova expelled them. Only while crossing interstellar space do planets and moons garner enough random electrons to render themselves much less ionized than the stars they eventually find themselves orbiting.

"Does anyone have a question before we break for lunch?"

James rose to his feet to ask, "Please, Kaidan, I beg you to explain one more mystery first. As you no doubt know, extremely distant regions of the cosmos feature **quasars**—objects that remain extremely bright despite their distance. Assuming that quasars, like ordinary stars and galaxies, consist only of hydrogen and helium, what enables a quasar to sustain an output of energy that is thousands of times greater than supernovae are able to produce for brief intervals?"

Kaidan responded: "As surely as the matter cosmos long ago stopped contracting and began expanding, so also the exterior antimatter bubble long ago stopped expanding and began contracting. Our outermost ordinary stars, enveloped by an incoming mist of anti-hydrogen and anti-helium, have long been melding with that mist, thus sourcing the incredible brightness of quasars. Examine quasars closely and you will find that they are all slightly brighter on the same side. That extra brightness is a forensic evidence of the rotational difference between the quasar, which is made of matter, and the enveloping mist, which is made of antimatter.

"Friends, "this completes my morning presentation. Lunch is provided in the atrium. We will reconvene at the start time noted in your Symposium brochure. Do enjoy your mid-day break!"

With that, Kaidan strode off-stage.

Photo A: Globular Cluster Omega Centauri (STScI-PRC2008-14)
http://hubblesite.org/newscenter/archive/releases/2008/14/image/a/
Credit: NASA,   ESA,   and   the   Hubble   Heritage   Team
(STScI/AURA)

Globular cluster Omega Centauri's core glitters with the light of 2
million stars—part of 10 million stars in one of the most massive
of +/- 200 globular clusters orbiting the Milky Way Galaxy.

Omega Centauri lies 17,000 light-years from Earth.

Photo B: Elliptical Galaxy NGC 2787 (STScI-2002-07)
http://hubblesite.org/newscenter/archive/releases/2002/07/image/a/
Credit: NASA and The Hubble Heritage Team (STScI/AURA)

Though labeled as an elliptical galaxy, dark bands at its equator reveal that reversing magnetic fields are changing NGC 2787 into a *spiral* galaxy. As more MFRs eject more mass, NGC 2787's nucleus will shrink and grow dimmer. Its dark bands will grow more apparent. For a photo of the same process at an even earlier stage, see NGC 4589 at

http://hubblesite.org/newscenter/archive/releases/2015/28/image/c/

Photo C: Barred Spiral Galaxy NGC 1300 (STScI-PRC2005-01)
http://hubblesite.org/gallery/album/galaxy/spiral/pr2005001a/
Credit: NASA,   ESA,   and   the   Hubble   Heritage   Team
(STScI/AURA)

Instead of spiraling immediately after they emerge from a nucleus, some galaxy arms delay spiraling until they first form a straight bar projecting from opposite sides of a nucleus. Assumedly all such bars have to form at relatively high speeds so as not to lag to any noticeable degree behind the ongoing spin of the ejecting nucleus. That is one reason why all similar straight bars in galaxies are posited here as resulting from gravity reversals on a galactic-scale.

M87, another elliptical galaxy with a jet of stars projecting straight out from an as-yet extremely bright nucleus, depicts an earlier stage of this same process. To see a photo of M87 on the Hubble website, visit
http://hubblesite.org/newscenter/archive/releases/1992/01/image/a/

Observe that the outermost tip of M87's straight jet has already begun to bend away in a new direction. A similar straight jet with a tip bending away in an opposite direction may already exist on the opposite side of M87 while remaining hidden behind M87's extremely bright nucleus.

Photo D: Pillars and Jets in HH 901/902 (STScI-2010-13)
http://hubblesite.org/gallery/album/nebula/pr2010013c/
Credit: NASA, ESA, and M. Livio and the Hubble 20th Anniversary Team (STScI)

Exploding supernovae expel jets of heavy matter unsuited for stars; magnetic pole reversals coalesce new planets instead. Once planets form, ensuing pole reversals expel them randomly on long interstellar treks to be caught by distant stars and added to far-away solar systems. Arrows highlight a few of the already expelled planets and planet-forming jets in this view.

Photo E: V838 Monocerotis (STScI-2003-10)
http://hubblesite.org/gallery/album/star/nova/pr2003010d/
Credit: NASA, ESA and H.E. Bond (STScI)

Mystery: How can a star explode so as to get rid of opaque *heavy* elements yet retain its hydrogen at home base so as to keep on shining, almost as if the star had not exploded at all, as in this pic of V838 Monocerotis?

For the explanation posed by Kaidan, see page 78.

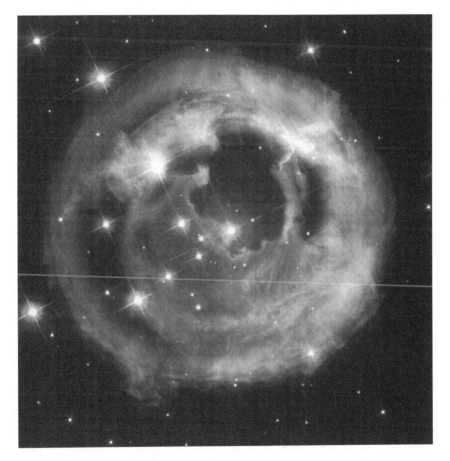

Photo F: The Cat's Eye Nebula (STScI-PRC2004-27)
http://hubblesite.org/newscenter/archive/releases/2004/27/image/a/
Credit: NASA, ESA, HEIC, and The Hubble Heritage Team
(STScI/AURA)

To learn (1) how the 'Cat's Eye' can keep expelling heavy matter while retaining enough hydrogen to keep on shining and (2) why both outer jets keep altering direction as indicated by the arrows, read pp. 78-94. Each jet has enough mass to form a planet. Neither jet is massive enough to form a new star like the one that ejected them yet still shines!

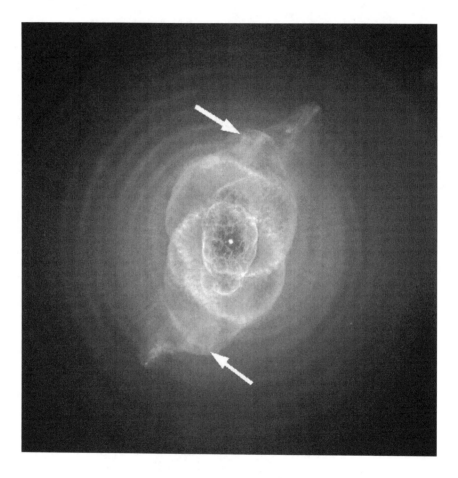

Photo G: Carina Nebula with heavy-element jets (STScI-2010-29)
http://hubblesite.org/newscenter/archive/releases/2010/29/image/a/
Credit: NASA, ESA, and the Hubble Heritage Project
(STScI/AURA)

Magnetic field reversals, unlike gravity, keep revectoring expelled globs of ionized matter until planets form. Left to right, how many corners do you see that are similar to those indicated by Kaidan's 3 white arrows?

Photo H: Part of Monkey Head Nebula NGC 2174 (STScI-2014-18)
http://hubblesite.org/newscenter/archive/releases/2014/18/image/a/
Credit: NASA, ESA, and the Hubble Heritage Team
(STScI/AURA)

In just this one part of the Monkey Head Nebula, dozens of visible jets expelled by MFRs send planets and moons on their way to be captured by the gravity of distant stars. Imagine more jets hidden inside or behind these immense clouds of heavy matter. MFRs, on a much smaller scale, are a natural version of the same magnetic force the US Navy's Zumwalt warships exploit to shoot shells as far as 63 nautical miles! Astronomers tell us stars form by *accumulating* mass in nebulae such as these, but what we actually see are solid nodes of heavy planet-forming matter *losing* mass as they leave some of it trailing away behind them.

Chapter Ten
The Origin of Matter and Energy

Striding into the back of the Symposium venue after a quick lunch, a leg stretch and a brain rest, Kent encountered a bearded Jewish rabbi standing near a bearded Muslim imam. Their name tags identified them as Ari Feinberg and Abu Kalama Abdullah. Kent shook hands with Rabbi Feinberg and then reached toward Imam Abdullah for a handshake. Examining Kent's name tag, Abdullah avoided Kent's hand with not even so much as a smile.

"I suppose," Kent offered, "that you both, like me, hope our ambassador from Arkona, along with imparting knowledge on cosmology, will soon affirm belief in God as well."

The Mullah replied brusquely, "We Muslims believe Allah has commissioned this heavenly messenger to do much more than merely affirm belief in Him. He has come to dispel Christianity's novel belief that God is three gods who are One, both now and forever. You will see!"

Abu Kalama Abdullah brushed past Kent and the rabbi, heading toward the coffee urns. Shaking his head in surprise, Rabbi Feinberg muttered, "Day 1, and already a line has been drawn in a sand dune blowing in from who knows where in the Mid-East. But, as I'm sure you are well aware, Dr. Madison, Judaism objects just as strongly that no man born of a woman should ever claim to be God or that the true God can possibly be three Persons who are nevertheless one."

Kent nodded with a look of sorrow. Then, eager to hear Becky's response to Kaidan's morning of teaching, Kent dialed her number on his phone.

Before Kent could ask, Becky exclaimed, "Darling, I find myself grasping so much more about magnetism, supernovae, gravity, globular clusters, galaxies and solar systems that I either forgot or never knew and which I wouldn't have cared about if left to myself. I'm thrilled! And I'm so proud that you, Dear, are there in person, breathing air in the same room with a master teacher from another world. But tell me, Kent, what are *you* thinking?"

After a pause, Kent replied, "Honey, for sure the science Kaidan expounds is clearly expressed and amazingly innovative. And I'm delighted to see the seeming openness to his teaching by many at the Symposium, including James Engle, a former friend with whom I had lost touch. But I can't help wondering…"

"Wondering what, Dear?" Becky pressed.

"…if our visitor from Arkona will prove to be just an interstellar version of James Engle, someone who is fascinated by creation but—by dismissing God and moral law—allows only for matter, energy and the laws of physics."

"You still want to be vindicated, don't you?"

"Vindicated? By whom? To prove what?" Kent shot back.

"Vindicated by Kaidan to prove to James Engle that he was wrong to chide you all those years ago for choosing theology when you could have mastered cosmology."

Irked by her comment, Kent was suddenly grateful to be distracted by someone tapping at his elbow.

"If so, would that be a wrong desire? Wait, Becky, someone else here is desperate to chat with me before Kaidan returns. I'll call you later. Bye!"

Kent turned to find a man who appeared to be from India. Gripping both Kent and Dr. Stansfield by the arms, he muttered:

"Something very strange is happening."

Kent saw a badge on the man's lapel, a badge labeled with three words below his name: HINDI TEXT TRANSLATOR.

"What troubles you," Stansfield asked.

"I'm responsible to translate as text whatever Mr. Kaidan presents in English on the middle screen over to the screen reserved for Hindi," the fellow explained with a slight accent. "But something happened twice this morning that was very odd."

"Please explain," Kent requested.

"Hindi is my mother tongue and I type quickly, but finding Hindi equivalents for technical English terms, such as those related to cosmology, can be difficult. Twice today when it took me more than about three seconds to find a proper Hindi translation of something Mr. Kaidan said, suddenly the right Hindi words—the ones I was mentally groping for—appeared up there on the screen before I could type them on my computer keyboard!

"This has never happened before, Gentlemen, and it makes me feel strange. It's as if that big screen up there is *alive* and knows Hindi better than I do. It lets me do my job but if I'm too slow, it takes over and fills in the right words. The Arabic text translator in the cubicle next to me had the same experience three times just within the last hour. How can this be happening?"

Before Kent could reply, Dr. Stansfield responded caustically, "I suspect the organizers of this Symposium have planted backup translators around the forum, poised and ready to supply needed words whenever a mistranslation occurs or an occasional delay goes a little too long. Not that you and your fellow front-liners should count on their help."

Turning away wryly, Stansfield resumed a conversation he had been enjoying with a friend. Kent said to the translator:

"I'm sorry. I simply don't know what to say."

As the Hindi translator, still confused, turned and walked back to his computer console, Kent ambled toward a man he had been told earlier was in charge of the Symposium staff.

"Excuse me," Kent said. "I see these six specialists translating Kaidan's English text for the six non-English screens; but do you also have backup translators checking to see if Kaidan's messages are being both promptly and correctly interpreted and are they ready to type in extra words if needed?"

"No, we have no backup translators," the official replied. "The only other translators in this special Symposium are the other six whose task is interpreting not the *visual* but just the *auditory* part of Mr. Kaidan's teaching for radio transmission worldwide. Also, because of them, speakers of the six other languages are getting the gist of Mr. Kaidan's teaching via earphones."

A moment later, Kaidan reappeared. Kent Madison had no time to ponder the Hindi translator's problem further. He and dozens of others had to rush back to their seats in time to see Kaidan announce his next topic on all seven screens.

HOW VISIBLE MATTER AROSE
FROM INVISIBLE EXTENT

"I trust your break allowed all of you time for mental as well as physical refreshment," Kaidan resumed.

"Now, to help everyone grasp the intricacies of subatomic physics, first I must clarify the nature of this vast house of existence which we all indwell. I refer to what we on Arkona call the four-dimensional *extent continuum*, which I have already referred to a few times earlier. It is that union of four dimensions we all experience continuously—i.e., the union of *length, width, height* and *time*."

Kent and dozens of other scholars immediately keyed in essentially the same memo on laptops, smartphones and tablets: *On Earth: space-time continuum; on Arkona: extent continuum.*

How fitting, James Engle observed. 'Extent' specifies what length, width and height (the three dimensions of space) and time are! So how efficient to dub the combination of all four as the *'extent'* continuum. Why perpetuate Albert Einstein's hyphenated 'space-time'? 'Extent,' a lone noun, suffices. Clever! Kaidan's continuation called James back from his musing.

"Check almost any dictionary," Kaidan counseled, "and you will find the term 'continuum' defined as something consisting of components so unified *that they cannot be separated nor even separately discerned.*

"By that definition, observe that even something as solid as an alloy of several metals does not qualify to be called a 'continuum.' Melt any alloy and its component metals separate according to their atomic weights."

Even as Kaidan spoke, all seven screens showed a blowtorch under an imaginary smelter reducing an alloy of four metals—labeled as tin, nickel, copper and iron—to a liquid state. All four metals soon tiered according to their atomic weights. Mankind's first interstellar teacher went on to elaborate:

"By that same token, no 'smelter' anywhere can separate out just *length*, for example, as distinct from its three corollaries, width, height and time. In other words, please understand…"

Kaidan began enunciating his every word with a measured cadence—his way of signifying something he deemed of paramount importance. Sweeping the audience with a winsomely benign gaze, Kaidan continued.

"On Earth, this indivisible union of length, width, height and time has long been regarded as akin to *nothing*, probably because the continuum itself is invisible. We see objects and events occurring *in* the extent continuum; yet we cannot see, hear, taste, smell or feel the extent continuum itself. In fact, we all experience the extent continuum *directly*, i. e., *apart from our physical senses*.

"Actually, the extent continuum is the ultimate *opposite* of 'nothing'! I declare it to be so because the union of length, width, height and time—contrary to the usual perception of it as 'nothing'—is *infinitely solid*! So it is actually 'something'! Not even a block of iron can match the absolute solidness of extent."

He paused with a chuckle. "Even up here, I can see many puzzled looks around this large room. So consider *this* with me:

"If you could make yourself small enough, you would see *gaps* between atoms in a block of iron, smaller gaps between electrons and atomic nuclei and even smaller gaps between protons and neutrons in the nucleus of an iron atom. BUT, no degree of smallness can ever enable you to discern *gaps* separating bits of length, for example, from bits of the other three extent dimensions, nor can you see gaps separating bits of all four extent dimensions joined together.

"By definition, any 'gap' separating one bit of extent from another bit of extent would itself have to consist of extent!

"So—we must recognize the extent continuum as *infinitely non-particulate*! To put it another way, the extent continuum is infinitely *gapless*. As a result, the extent continuum cannot be torn inasmuch as it has no gap that could be enlarged to allow a tear. So, can any foreign physical substance ever be *inserted* into the extent continuum? The answer is 'No!' simply because the extent continuum has no gap that could be enlarged to accommodate any such insertion! That said, we should all be amazed that anything— whether it be a photon of light or a particle of matter—could ever *form* in, let alone *move through*, this infinitely solid continuum!

Yet matter and energy not only *exist in* but also ably *move within* the extent continuum. How can that happen?

"There is only one solution to this paradox: **both energy and matter exist not only _in_ but also _of_ the extent continuum**. Yet Doctors Tyson and Goldsmith, in accord with a typically human thought pattern, regard the origin of matter and energy as still undefined by claiming that light '...travels...the vacuum of space devoid of any supporting medium.'[20]

"Extent itself is both 'the supporting medium' and the *substance* of both light and matter just as an ocean is both 'the supporting medium' and the very *substance* of waves and tides. I will now explain how this happens.

"Although extent cannot be torn, it can be *stretched* or *contracted* provided every stretch is compensated by *an inversely equal contraction* and every contraction is accommodated by *an inversely equal stretch*!

ALTERED CIRCUMFERENCES = PHOTONS!

"Imagine the shape of a cylinder superimposed upon a volume of homogeneous extent. Imagine that the cylinder is 20 centimeters in circumference and 2 meters long. For that cylinder to move through the extent continuum the way a photon of energy moves, what has to happen inside the cylinder?

"Here is my answer: First, visualize a circle that is only a few centimeters in circumference centered on what is to be the lead face of the cylinder. Now make that cylinder move forward in the extent continuum the way a wave moves through water, except for this one difference, i.e., space momentarily encompassed by the cylinder as it moves *is no longer homogeneous! Instead, by the time the cylinder has moved its full two-meter length, space within the circle centered on the cylinder's leading face has increased to nearly double its circumference at midpoint and then diminished back to its original circumference as the cylinder moves on, leaving that space homogenous once more.*

"This increase in the size of the circle of course requires space elsewhere inside the cylinder to be squeezed to an inversely equal degree. By the way, the difference between the lesser and greater circumferences of the inner circle must always conform to the ratio known as the **golden mean**.

"Conversely, if the circle on the leading face of a cylinder begins with a *larger* circumference diminishing to a *smaller* circumference at midpoint, only to expand back to the *larger* circumference, that is an opposite kind of photon."

Clyde Smith suggested, "Kaidan, why not call the latter kind an *eso*-photon and the former kind an *exo*-photon?"

"An excellent suggestion, Clyde!" Kaidan replied. "And when either cylinder has moved *two* meters, all of the extent altered by its passage returns to homogeneity! In summary, each cylinder, while wave-moving *nothing more than a circumference* through stationary extent, becomes a photon moving at the speed of light. A cylinder's length defines a photon's wave-length. The girth of its internal circumferences determines its potency as energy. Next, please ponder what results when a cylinder in the extent continuum transports *something more* complex than a mere circumference.

ALTERED SPHERICAL VOLUMES = SUB-ATOMIC PARTICLES

"Finding that a photon is simply an altered **circumference** moving at the speed of light inside an extent cylinder, what shall we say of a cylinder that wave-moves an expanding or a contracting **spherical volume** as its altered extent 'cargo'? In that event, my friends, we are describing not a photon but a *particle* of matter or antimatter—an electron or a positron, for example—wave-moving at considerably *less* than the speed of light because it entails moving much more than a mere circumference."

Scanning the entire scientific contingent—the nearest portion of his Symposium audience—Kaidan said, "I must now ask you specialists in the science known as physics a series of questions I think you will find can be answered in terms of this new paradigm. First, what determines the **mass** of a particle when a particle is defined as nothing more than a tiny spherical volume shifting across the extent continuum?"

A scientist stood and, as an aide handed him a microphone, replied with a German accent, "As you have already told us, Herr Kaidan, increasing or decreasing the *girth* of a photon's **circumference** increases or decreases its energy. Thus I conclude the difference between the *original* homogenous spherical volume and the *altered* volume, whether greater or lesser, defines **mass**."

"Correct, Herr Gorman!" Kaidan replied. "Next: what determines whether a particle has positive or negative **charge**?"

This time a French physicist replied, "Monsieur Kaidan, if an **expanded** spherical volume of extent defines *positive* charge, then **contracted** spherical volume will define *negative* charge."

"Très bien, Monsieur François!" Kaidan responded. "And now, my third question takes us back to our earlier observation that matter and antimatter must always appear in the form of *particle-antiparticle pairs*. Would someone care to define—in terms of this paradigm—the difference between a particle and its antiparticle and why they must always appear as **pairs**?"

This time a Spanish scientist stood up to declare: "If one spherical volume of extent *expands* to form a particle, Señor Kaidan, an adjacent spherical volume of extent must *contract* to an inversely equal degree. Both together form a particle-antiparticle pair. Once formed, both components must separate oppositely in their respective wave-moving cylinders.

"The inverse equality of altered extent within a particle and its antiparticle is what gives them equal mass with opposite charge. That is also what makes it inevitable that they will co-annihilate as a blast of energy if by chance they get too close. It follows that two particles may have opposite charge; but if the amount of altered extent within them is inversely *unequal*, they are in no danger of co-annihilating because they are *not* a particle-antiparticle pair."

"Muy bien, Señor Talman," Kaidan responded, adding, "And now I have a fourth and perhaps more difficult question. It relates to the fact that subatomic particles are known to **spin**. How then can a particle—a spherical volume of either expanded or contracted extent wave-moving through the extent continuum—*spin* without shearing its surface free from the contiguous extent through which it is moving as a wave?"

This time an Australian scholar answered. "Most honored mate from Arkona, surely what spins is not the spherical volume of an entire particle, since that would require the extent continuum to shear. Rather, two points—one of greater and the other of lesser extent density alteration relative to the particle as a whole—must be 'wave-moving,' as you called it, <u>around a perimeter of the particle</u>. I picture these two points chasing each other like gerbils around the girth of a subatomic particle while remaining 180 degrees apart! This wave-movement, of course, is one that keeps occurring even while the particle itself is wave-moving about on its own trajectories."

"Excellent, Dr. Benton from Parkes Observatory in New South Wales! And now, finally," Kaidan asked, "will someone please tell me why, in terms of this new paradigm, matter and energy always remain subject to the full range of every conservation law in physics?"

A scientist from India responded, "Sahib Kaidan, as you explain, extent—though infinitely solid—can be expanded or contracted provided inverse equality is sustained. Could it be that balancing every contraction with an inversely equal expansion is what keeps conservation laws in effect everywhere, Sahib?"

"Well spoken, Sahib Aridi," Kaidan replied appreciatively.

Scholars with a modicum of scientific knowledge gasped as the significance of Kaidan's most recent definitions sank in. Clyde Smith was reflecting that physicists had long known that photons of energy and particles of matter both resemble waves. What stymied scholars was how to define why one wave is a *photon* that inherently moves at the speed of light and another wave is a *particle* that needs a push to move at all.

Kaidan had resolved both enigmas as nothing more than inversely equal alterations of circumferences versus spherical volumes wave-moving in extent continuum cylinders. The entity wherein both kinds of 'waves' move is also their substance.

First a grand cosmology and now mass, charge, antimatter, spin and conservation laws are defined for us as well! Clyde texted the Loop. *Surely this marvelous outpouring of new-to-us, uniquely multi-faceted insight cannot go on much longer.*

As Clyde was about to discover, Kaidan was not even close to exhausting his contingent of mind-expanding new paradigms.

THE FIVE FEATURES OF A SPHERE
AS A *UNIFYING MOTIF*

"Inasmuch as subatomic particles are nothing more than *spherical* volumes of altered extent," Kaidan went on to say, "respecting that relationship, I suggest we dub all subatomic particles generically as **spherons**. Particles consisting of *contracted* extent can thus be called *eso*-**spherons**. Others made of *expanded* extent are *exo*-**spherons**.

"So also photons of energy—recognized as expanded versus contracted *circumferences* propagating cylindrically via the extent continuum—can now be dubbed as *circumferences* or, specifically, **eso-circumferons** versus *exo*-**circumferons**!

"Circumference and spherical volume are, however, only two among the five main features of a sphere. The other three are *radius, diameter* and *surface area*. Could it possibly be true that radius, diameter and surface area join with spherical volume and circumference to comprise an actual, complete, even *unifying* motif underlying the entire cosmos?"

Brace yourselves, James texted everyone on the Loop. *This ultra-intellectual from Arkona may be about to unveil the most sought-after touchstone in history: a unifying premise that describes the entire physical universe in one statement. This is all so incredibly exhilarating.*

"Let me begin by asking your scientists which aspect of the entire physical universe conforms to the *radius* of a sphere," Kaidan queried. "I'll help you along by suggesting that you ask yourself: What does every radius connect to? And then visualize which force functions in ways corresponding to radii?"

As a television camera panned from astronomers to physicists to cosmologists to leaders in other fields of science, every countenance revealed the utmost mental focus. Kent sensed that every expert, perhaps unwittingly, was competing for fame as the one most able to anticipate the flow of Kaidan's logic.

THE RADIUS OF A SPHERE = *GRAVITY*

Clyde Smith, after several seconds of rapt thought, sprang from his chair, gripped the microphone offered by an aide and said almost tremulously: *"Gravity!* As you said, Kaidan, gravity is a *radial* force with a bi-directional propensity. If gravity is not pulling matter *toward* a center of mass **eso-radially**, it is expelling matter away from that center of mass **exo-radially**."

"Indeed, we have already encountered eso-gravity and exo-gravity," Kaidan approved, "but now what else in the cosmos corresponds to a *diameter* of a sphere?"

THE DIAMETER OF A SPHERE = *MAGNETISM*

Homer Grassley, drawing a circle on a notepad, sketched a line across its middle and stared at it. *Which feature of the cosmos corresponds to that line?* he asked himself. A moment later, Homer, not even waiting for a microphone, called aloud. *"Magnetism!* Magnetic poles—equidistant from the *center* of a magnetic field—are either attracting matter *to* or repelling matter *from* opposite poles located at the ends of a *diameter* of a sphere!"

"Well said, Homer," Kaidan nodded, repeating Homer's assertion for the benefit of those who had not heard his mic-less reply. "Thus a magnetic pole that attracts particles made of *expanded* extent can be called an **exo-pole** whereas the opposite end of the diameter—the one attracting particles made of contracted extent—is an **eso-pole**. Finally, we have only to identify something that naturally conforms to *spherical surface areas*. Do I hear any suggestions?"

Silence reigned in the Symposium, leaving Kaidan to reply rhetorically: "Tell me, terra-physicists in this Symposium; tell me something about protons and neutrons in the nuclei of heavier elements. Do they jumble together like golf balls in a bag or are they much more organized than that?"

"They form concentric hollow spheres!" Clyde Smith shouted. "Yes, of course; that is how spherical surface area shows up in the subatomic world." Kaidan posted a response on-screen:

SPHERICAL SURFACE AREAS = *ATOMIC STRUCTURE*

"What of electrons orbiting atomic nuclei?" Kaidan probed further. "Do they orbit nuclei at *random* distances or at discrete distances?"

"Despite the fact that negative charge repels negative charge," James Engle called aloud, "electrons manage to orbit the nuclei of atoms jointly while maintaining discrete distances from the nuclei. Thus they too, merely by their motion, describe concentric spherical surface areas in the exterior of atoms."

"May we agree, then," Kaidan asked, "that *closed* concentric spheres made of nucleons in the nuclei of atoms should be dubbed **eso-surface areas**? May we also agree that *open* concentric spheres described by *electrons* confined to discrete orbits *outside* atomic nuclei may be dubbed as **exo-surface areas**?"

Nearly all Symposium participants applauded in response.

"Thank you, Everyone," Kaidan responded. "Please observe also that these same five features of a sphere are also manifest at *macro* levels of the cosmos, as I will explain next.

THE FIVE FEATURES OF A SPHERE *IN THE COSMOS*!

"So also, in the origin of the cosmos, dark energy's contracting space-time *within* the sphere of origin and expanding space-time *exterior* to the SOO became an **eso-volume** and an **exo-volume** on a macro level. As I have stated, these two forms of dark energy switched places just prior to the Great Cosmic Confluence.

"Likewise, when the matter bubble and the antimatter bubble separated—one inwardly and the other outwardly from the sphere of origin—the outer bubble formed a macro-cosmic *exo-surface area*. The inner bubble became a macro-cosmic *eso-surface* area.

"The inner part of the axis on which the matter cosmos is spinning clockwise forms a macro-cosmic *eso-pole*. Exterior parts of that same axis whereon the antimatter cosmos is spinning anticlockwise form a macro-cosmic *exo-pole*. Likewise, just as one magnetic pole *attracts* a certain kind of matter while the opposite pole *repels* the same form of matter, so also one end of the eso-diameter of the matter cosmos is drawing galaxies toward it at an unusual rate. That is something terra-cosmologists have already discovered. They call it 'The Great Attractor.' Eventually you will also discover a distant counterpart waiting to be described as 'The Great Repeller'—an area where the other end of the eso-diameter of the cosmos is pushing galaxies away.

"Initially, the prevailing radial motion of every particle of matter *toward* the cosmic center sustained a macro-cosmic **eso-radial** phenomenon. The initial motion of every particle of antimatter *away* from the cosmic center sustained a macro-cosmic **exo-radial** counterpart. Recall that these two phenomena reversed concurrent with the Great Cosmic Confluence.

"Fifth and finally, the *clockwise* motion of every particle of matter—which led to conserved angular momentum during the matter cosmos' contraction phase—provided the macro-cosmos with an **eso-circumferential** phenomenon. Likewise the *anti-clockwise* motion of every particle of antimatter during the antimatter cosmos' initial expansion phase became an **exo-circumferential** feature for the macro-cosmos.

"These two phenomena also reversed their eso- and exo-motions concurrent with the Great Cosmic Confluence.

"I will have more to say later about this five-fold motif underlying the entire physical cosmos, but first I must explain the special nature of **quarks**!"

Chapter Eleven
The Unique Nature of Quarks

HOW QUARKS DIFFER FROM
ELECTRONS AND POSITRONS

"So much for the origin of photons on one hand, electrons and positrons on the other," Kaidan resumed. "But now, as you are about to learn, *quarks* derive from a rather different basis. Photons, electrons and positrons differ from quarks in that the former roam sectors of the cosmos freely. Quarks are found only inside hadrons, the most common form of which here in the matter cosmos are protons and neutrons.

"Beyond that aspect, quarks are remarkably unique in another way. Whether it is the gravitational attraction twixt the Earth and a passing asteroid or the electromagnetic attraction that pulls electrons closer to protons, either attraction is strongest close-up and weaker as the distance between any two such objects increases. Conversely, the force that binds any two quarks together inside protons and neutrons is *relaxed* close up but grows ever stronger if the distance between any two quarks of opposite charge increases by even the slightest margin!

"As a result, when particle accelerators smash protons against each other with great force, quarks inside the protons separate minimally for a nanosecond; but even then they do not separate far enough long enough for terra-physicists to fully discern what distinguishes one quark from its fellows!

"If the bond between quarks were merely *electrical*, like the attraction between electrons and protons," Kaidan added, "collisions in a particle accelerator could *obliterate* protons and neutrons by disassembling the quarks that comprise them.

"But if a particle accelerator—a device made by mortals—could destroy protons and neutrons that easily, surely the ultra-high temperatures and pressures in the interior of *exploding stars* would destroy protons and neutrons even more readily.

"Instead of linking protons and neutrons to make the heavy elements needed for more complex phenomena, exploding stars would simply *destroy* myriad protons and neutrons. A process that destructive, besides leaving the cosmos with less and less hydrogen and helium over time, would also leave the cosmos with zero heavy elements for its further development."

James Engle frowned, admitting to himself that he had never thought of the indestructibility of protons in a particle accelerator as portending the need for protons to be indestructible in the interior of exploding stars.

"Physicists call that powerful quark-to-quark attraction **the strong force**," Kaidan continued. "The strong force is said to bind quarks together by means of bridge-like particles known as **gluons**. Physicists also find that quarks, unlike electrons and positrons, come in six varieties! Lacking insight as to the nature of each variety of quark, physicists simply dub them with *pro tem* names that sound almost as whimsical as the name 'quark' itself. Thus one kind of quark is said to manifest *'Charm.'* Still another is credited with *'Strangeness.'* The four others are designated as *'Up'* and *'Down'* and *'Top'* and *'Bottom'* quarks.

"As a final feature of this already complex mystery, some terra-physicists, grappling with something known as 'string theory,' contend they seem to be finding **'extra dimensions'** down at the quark level of the universe.

"Think of that invincible quark-to-quark attraction as one which, by making protons and neutrons indestructible, enables exploding stars to larder the cosmos with heavy elements. Surely that strong force is something we need to understand. And I assume every physicist on Earth would be pleased if those six strange quark descriptors—charm, strangeness, up, down, top and bottom—could also be defined.

"Likewise, if what appear to be 'extra' dimensions fluttering among quarks could also be categorized, would not that also be a major leap forward for terra-science? So I ask, do you want me to explain these mysteries?"

Scores of Symposium members arose, responding in their multiple languages, "Yes! Please explain these mysteries!"

Startled by such unexpected spontaneity, James Engle scanned the Symposium audience in awe. Only a short time before, easily 90 percent of 500 or so attendees would hardly have given quarks, gluons, 'strangeness,' 'charm' and other quark features a second thought. Yet Kaidan, with ease, had subtly imparted not only an up-to-date summary of what is *known* about quarks, but also—and even more incredibly—a virtual public *demand* to have the as-yet unexplained nature of the quark conundrum expounded at once!

Again, we see we are in the presence of a master teacher, Justine Hobbs texted to everyone on the Loop. Philosopher Stansfield texted agreement. Engineer Clyde Smith shot back, *Who would have thought this austere Symposium could suddenly turn into a pep rally for a proper understanding of quarks! After a build-up like this, Kaidan better be able to explain every part of the quark conundrum or protest may break out worldwide!*

Kent, caught up in the awe of the moment, noticed that even Charles Stein, that hard-to-impress atheist, was standing tall and gazing at Kaidan expectantly. James Engle, along with other experts in the physical sciences, was also nodding in response.

Surely, James Engle groaned inwardly, *Kaidan could not tantalize mankind with so lucid a summary of the quark conundrum and then leave the essential nature of quarks undefined. Surely not!*

Then came a never-to-be-forgotten moment when engrossed attendees at the Symposium, plus millions of other Earth citizens viewing and listening via worldwide media, sighed with relief to hear Kaidan's next statement.

"It is now my choice privilege," he assured his vast audience, "to bestow a gift of knowledge from the 24-planet Federation that I serve as an ambassador. First, let me offer terra-physicists a key they can use to replace their six whimsical quark descriptors with definitive titles. This key will also explain why extra dimensions seem to be showing up in the quark realm."

James Engle, turning to Homer Grassley, quipped, "Sounds like you won't have to donate a kidney and a lung after all, Homer."

"Taking the familiar for granted," Kaidan continued, "is a hindrance to the advancement of science. The more familiar something becomes, the less likely we are to investigate it thoroughly. So what could be more familiar to all—hence more likely to be ignored—than this omnipresent extent continuum that encompasses us and all the cosmos with length, width, height and time? Mankind is overdue to discover its hidden complexities!

COMPLEXITY WITHIN THE EXTENT CONTINUUM

"People of Earth, my duty and privilege here and now is to inform you that this marvel we call the extent continuum is much more complex than you have as yet realized. I stand here to aver that the four-dimensional extent continuum universally embraces four *sub-extent continua within itself!*

"First, we have **sub-extent continuum A**, a base where *length* becomes fully endowed with width, height and time.

"Joined to sub-extent continuum A is also **sub-extent continuum B**, a second base where *width* becomes fully endowed with length, height and time. Next, recognize also **sub-extent continuum C**, a base where *height* becomes fully endowed with length, width and time. Last but equally significant, we must recognize also **sub-extent continuum D**, a base whereby *time* becomes fully endowed with length, width and height."

Until that day, Justine realized, "dimensions" and "continua" were little more to her than words in a lexicon. Now, under Kaidan's teaching, both terms were coming alive with deep significance. At first she thought, *this is not my field. I probably won't use this information, so I don't need to stretch my mind to absorb such far-out concepts,* followed by, *No! I want to understand!* And, to her delight, she did!

"We, on our level of the cosmos," Kaidan was saying, "experience all four sub-extent continua *as one.* So also do electrons and positrons. Quarks, however, are much more limited in that each kind of quark exists *primarily* in *only two* of the four above-described sub-extent continua. Each quark likewise exists only *secondarily* in the other two sub-extent continua.

"That said, no single quark exists primarily in all four sub-extent continua as do electrons, for example. That is why a quark, unlike an electron, cannot wave-move inside a *single* extent cylinder. Rather, three quarks must wave-move together in at least three co-joined extent cylinders.

"But why should it matter at all to the cosmos that quarks be so uniquely fashioned? Let me explain.

"Because of the above limitations, each quark lacks *part* of what primary existence in all four sub-extent continua provides— that is, *full* dimensional existence. Ergo any one quark, to gain dimensional completeness, absolutely *must* maintain bridge-like connections—i.e., **gluons**—with at least two other equally incomplete quarks so as to achieve the ideal of four-dimensional completeness *jointly*, via mutual sharing.

"Given their need for dimensional completeness, the mutual attraction that binds any three quarks to form either a proton or a neutron cannot be anything other than hyper-strong!

"As to why there are *six* kinds of quarks, note that six is the maximum number of pairings of A, B, C and D sub-extent continua that can possibly occur, as we find in the following list, which I now post for you on all seven screens:

#1 quark exists primarily in sub-extent continua **A** and **B**.
#2 quark exists primarily in sub-extent continua **A** and **C**.
#3 quark exists primarily in sub-extent continua **A** and **D**.
#4 quark exists primarily in sub-extent continua **B** and **C**.
#5 quark exists primarily in sub-extent continua **B** and **D**.
#6 quark exists primarily in sub-extent continua **C** and **D**.

"Match these six pairings to strangeness, charm, up, down, top and bottom and each of your six whimsical *pro tem* quark identifiers will enjoy objective definition at last!

"But what about those extra dimensions some physicists claim exist in the quark realm? Let me assure you--what they are really finding is simply the same familiar four—length, width, height and time—showing up again and again, as it were, in the four distinct sub-extent continua: A, B, C and D!

"Seekers of truth here on Earth, now you know!"

As Kaidan paused, virtually the entire Symposium audience surged to its feet with avid response. Kent perceived that most participants were clapping and cheering to express nothing less than genuine amazement over Kaidan's strikingly clear presentation. Kent sensed even more gusto this time than in previous outbursts of adulation for Kaidan's deft expositions.

Kent saw various participants applauding yet casting cautious glances at the several dozen specialists in the physical sciences, virtually all of them world famous and seated front and center in the forum, looking straight up at Kaidan. It seemed to Kent that hundreds of minds pondering the same question made it almost audible while still unspoken.

That question was: *Will Earth's top astrophysicists and subatomic experts, many of whom have designed and worked with particle accelerators and bubble chambers, fully accept star-man Kaidan's marvelously unique way of explaining the quark conundrum? Surely they know that what this visitor from beyond Pluto and the Oort cloud has been explaining hour by hour renders books they've authored, lectures they've delivered and awards they've been granted, passé!*

Justine Hobbs was thinking, *If James and these other physical scientists down in front throw Kaidan's explanation straight back at him, how will he react? If Kaidan takes offense, no doubt 24 other worlds are on his side, for goodness sake. Earth is seriously out-numbered here!*

Then it happened. Kent, Justine and hundreds of other Symposium participants, virtually as one, sighed with relief as more and more members of the physical sciences contingent rose to their feet and joined the applause.

Many were nodding with approval and even smiling. But was it really nothing more than protocol? Kaidan was, after all, no less than an interstellar ambassador, someone to be given at least a deferential respect.

James Engle was gripped by profound awe. Initially, shocked by Kaidan's way of solving the quark conundrum, he had barely restrained a snort, thinking *who in all of academia will believe that mere dimensions within the extent continuum can interact so profoundly as to form four sub-extent continua?* Then, a moment later, reviewing his thoughts, James chided himself, thinking, *How dare an academic of my status be so arrogant as to attach a derisive adjective like 'mere' to the extent continuum?*

After all, that was Kaidan's main point, was it not? James mused further. *Perhaps mistaking our partial knowledge of the extent continuum for the complete story has indeed kept us from discerning facts that are patently obvious to who knows how many trillions of thinkers in those 24 other hyper-advanced societies represented by Kaidan.*

Sighing acceptance, James texted his fellow panelists plus Kent via the Loop, opining: *Kaidan's totally alien explanation of the quark conundrum reeks disturbingly of logic and elegance!*

Subsequently, his phone, and Kent's, buzzed with Justine's prompt texted response. Both men looked down to read her reply: *For you physical science bods, Kaidan's solution to the quark issue is just subatomic physics. For me, it confirms the best way to administer psychotherapy to depressed people! Just as quarks need four-dimensional completeness, don't we also need to bond together for intellectual and emotional completeness along with unity of purpose so that society may endure?*

"Friends, with these last few comments my presentation on cosmology and subatomic physics is complete," Kaidan commented. As much as I have enjoyed helping mankind understand the origin of the cosmos and deeper aspects of subatomic physics, my primary motivation in visiting planet Earth is something else, something that ranks far higher on the scale of cosmic significance than everything I have presented thus far.

"That will be our topic beginning tomorrow at 9 a.m."

Both Charles Stein and Kent Madison received Kaidan's final comment as a basis for hope. Several rows behind them, Rabbi Ari Feinberg and Sunni Muslim Abu Kalama Abdullah were also rapt with anticipation.

"And so I conclude my teaching for today," Kaidan stated, adding: "I bid my listeners here in this Symposium and around the world to ponder what I have said. Good day!"

AN OMINOUS WARNING

As soon as the Symposium dismissed, Imam Abdullah strode over to the cubicle where Salim Kumer, the Arabic translator, sat exhausted behind his equipment. Speaking to Salim in Arabic, Abu Kalama said, "As I told you earlier, the word from Saudi Arabia is that we believe Kaidan is a forerunner of the Mahdi who will complete the mission of the Prophet, peace be upon him! But if we are wrong—if tomorrow Kaidan begins to say anything confirming Judaism, Christianity, Hinduism or any other religion—look across to me. If I give you this sign...."

Abdullah sliced the edge of his hand across his throat.

"...you must stop your translating at once. This is a fatwa you must obey on pain of death!"

"I understand," Salim responded.

ON CNN THAT EVENING

"Well, Everyone," Greg Moore said after re-introducing CNN's evening panel of members fresh from the Symposium, "indications are that in the USA alone, 94 million people viewed Kaidan and the proceedings on television alone while no one knows how many tens of millions more tuned in by television and radio worldwide. Airlines, finding that myriad passengers were calling to cancel reservations so as not to miss the Symposium, hastily announced that event proceedings would be available on board and online except during landings and takeoffs, of course.

"Also, within the last two hours, six polls indicate that most respondents who regarded Big Bang Cosmology as a viable theory now question or even dismiss it as illogical and/or scientifically untenable. Blogs, chat rooms and social media sites worldwide reveal myriad participants who—if they could—would like to say to scientists, in effect—'Keep your theory that two billion universes of mass, half of it matter and half of it antimatter, had to co-annihilate to spare this one cosmos. We don't believe it.'

"Many survey participants report they cannot accept Alan Guth's theory that the infant cosmos expanded millions of times faster than the speed of light just to sidestep becoming a black hole and then suddenly halt in violation of conservation of momentum.

"Virtually every poll respondent who has pondered Kaidan's 'Six Dubious Quick Fixes' says he or she finds Kaidan's Sphere of Origin cosmology far more appealing than BBC. What are your thoughts on the Symposium thus far, William?"

"First and foremost," William Stansfield replied, "Kaidan's lack of any reference thus far to a divine being—i.e., to a 'God' as most commonly named—has greatly encouraged atheists and Communist governments. Even if some form of theism should emerge as part of Kaidan's presentation tomorrow, Muslims, Judaists and Christians in particular should be wary of expecting our extra-terrestrial visitor to affirm any specific doctrines in the Torah, the Bible and/or in the Koran."

"Kaidan's mind," Justine added, "appears exclusively linked to strictly logical connections, which as we all know are relatively rare in texts penned long before the birth of modern science. So topics religious people see as important, such as miracles, the need to atone for human sin, resurrection, eternal life, etc., have no doubt been long abandoned by such an advanced extraterrestrial society as Arkona, if in fact they were ever even considered by such societies."

"As for me," Charles Stein interposed, "if Kaidan does affirm belief in God in any way, I will want to ask him the same question atheist Bertrand Russell said he would ask God if he were to meet such a being after death. Russell reportedly said he would ask, 'Sir, why did you not give me better evidence?'"

That was as far as Kent, listening to CNN from his hotel room bed, got. His wife Becky, lying beside him, heard him breathing the way a sleeper breathes while recovering from sheer mental and emotional exhaustion. Easing the remote control from Kent's hand, she flicked off the television and fell asleep from her own almost-equal exhaustion.

Chapter Twelve
The Ultimate Unrecognized Corollary

At 9:00 the next morning, Symposium attendees welcomed Kaidan for Day 2. "Yesterday," Kaidan began, "my goal was to enhance mankind's grasp of cosmology and subatomic physics all the way from 1) the separation of matter from antimatter at the sphere of origin, 2) the Great Cosmic Confluence, 3) dark energy's reversal, 4) eso- and exo-gravity, 5) why galaxies come in different shapes, 6) the four sub-extent continua and 7) even why quarks bond so strongly. Yet all such knowledge combined is merely a prelude to the grandest and most important insight of all.

"People of planet Earth, the time has come for me to tell you that this four-dimensioned extent continuum—in which and of which all matter and energy exist—is not alone! Rather, this amazing extent continuum, which we all know is real despite its intrinsic invisibility, co-exists with its own equally invisible yet just as real corollary. Your dictionaries define a corollary as a proposition deduced from another that has been proved. Thus a profound continuum comprised of three infinite *value* dimensions —*intellect, emotion and will*—brings completion to the one continuum consisting only of length, width, height and time."

Kent Madison, Charles Stein, Ari Feinberg and Abu Kalama Abdullah tensed on their chairs. At last! At last! At last! Kent sighed. Kaidan seemed to be broaching the subject of God with just one fateful option yet to be determined: which earthly view of God, if any, would Arkona's view of Him confirm or at least resemble? Was Kaidan's "Value Continuum" nothing more than an alias for Stephen Spielberg's innocuously impersonal "force," or would it designate Someone sublimely immanent?

"Just as length, breadth, height and time enable us," Kaidan asserted, "to experience varying degrees of *extension*, so also the

Value Continuum's three universal value coordinates are what enable us to *discern* degrees of **logic**, *experience* a varying range of **emotions** and *apply* varying degrees of freewill **initiative**. Whereas we as finite beings experience these three values finitely, the Value Continuum sources all three *infinitely*.

"Infinite *intellect* renders the Value Continuum **omniscient**. His infinite capacity to respond with emotion renders him **omnisentient**. Infinite *will* qualifies him as **omnipotent**. That said, the Value Continuum is just as totally personal as the extent continuum is *impersonal*.

"As pertains to terra-philosophy, Baruch Spinoza is credited with striving to harmonize science with theology centuries ago. Yet even Spinoza, by misperceiving an empty vacuum as *nothing*, failed to recognize it instead as a four-dimensional continuum needing another continuum as its corollary. Isaac Newton, for his part, recognized the continuum but was content to leave it illogically without a corollary! Even Albert Einstein allowed the same blind spot to persist.

"Today it is my privilege to pronounce mankind's age-long blind spot *insighted*! Just as the invisible extent continuum enables us to experience degrees of presence and duration, so also the equally invisible Value Continuum enables us to recognize degrees of value, respond to discerned value with degrees of emotion and act according to what we see and feel with varying degrees of initiative. Each of these two continua is the eternally rightful corollary of the other. A truly omniscient, omnisentient, omnipotent Value Continuum who is forever omnipresent in space and time truly does exist!

"As you might expect, there are ways in which the Value Continuum and the extent continuum are profoundly alike and other ways in which they are profoundly different. Let me explain.

TWO INFINITE CONTINUA:
SO ALIKE YET SO DIFFERENT!

"As you recall," Kaidan reminisced, "I explained how the total inter-relatedness of the four extent dimensions assures four sub-extent continua within the extent continuum. I also revealed how every aspect of the six kinds of quarks derives from certain combinations of the four sub-extent continua. You all saw how six kinds of quarks result. I explained how the mutual attraction that keeps triplets of quarks bonded together is what makes protons as durable as the cosmos itself! I even divulged why what seem to be extra dimensions in the quark domain are simply length, width, height and time reappearing in the four sub-extent contexts.

"People of Earth, do you recall how I unveiled these mysteries for you?"

As though with one voice, many in the symposium audience exclaimed "Yes!"

"Did you thank me for explaining these mysteries?"

Again, the audience called a positive "Yes," this time with some wariness. All sensed that Kaidan was leading them to the brink of something that might startle them. What might that be?

"Does anyone in this august gathering anticipate what I am about to declare that is closely akin to what you thanked me for yesterday?" Kaidan asked.

Silence reigned. Not one scientist who had readily responded to Kaidan the day before knew what he might be trolling for now via this latest question. Only Dr. Kent Madison saw where Kaidan's logic was leading. Slowly he rose to his feet for the first time amid this, the grandest intellectual convocation in history.

Television cameras around the edges of the Symposium swiveled to focus on Kent as an aisle attendant handed him a microphone. In a hotel across Manhattan, Becky Madison gasped and pleaded, "Darling, please, please don't embarrass yourself." Faculty members and students at Founders University in Virginia stared at their TV screens with a mixture of tension and awe.

As for James, Justine and everyone else in the Loop, they were wondering where Kent, a theologian, had found the backbone to speak up in what had been, up to that moment at least, an exclusive enclave for experts in hard physical sciences.

"Kaidan," Kent began, gripping the microphone as if it embodied the gift of life itself. "First you explained that four sub-extent continua arise from the blending of four extent dimensions within the extent continuum. May we likewise conclude that three *sub-Value Continua* similarly result from a mutual inter-dimensional sharing among the three infinite value dimensions—intellect, emotion and will—within the Value Continuum?"

Kaidan, devoid of expression, descended from the dais.

"Surely, due to that comparable interaction," Kent added, "the dimension of omniscience must also be omnisentient and omnipotent, hence must be recognized as a *divine* Person."

Kaidan, expressionless, was now stepping closer to Kent.

"The dimension of omnisentience, likewise due to that akin interaction," Kent said, "must also possess omniscience and omnipotence, hence he too must be lauded as a second divine Person. Finally and identically, the dimension of omnipotence, rendered eternally omniscient as well as omnisentient via that akin dimensional sharing, must also be a *third* divine Person.

"Yet these three ever-so-real though invisible Personas together comprise *one* ever-so-real though invisible divine Person! Hence just as the four-dimensional extent continuum is one continuum with four sub-extent continua—without which the physical sciences would have no quarks, hence no protons and neutrons—in like manner the three-dimensional Value Continuum *cannot be anything other than three Persons who are one Person!*

"Tell me, Kaidan, am I correct?"

Kaidan beckoned Kent to join him in the aisle. Kaidan gripped Kent's wrist, raised his arm high and declared, "Dr. Kent Madison, I could not have said that better myself. Ladies and gentlemen worldwide, what Dr. Madison has articulated for us has long been, for this one planet only, a strategically hidden but ultimately significant missing corollary—the triune Value Continuum. *At long last mankind has found a very primary and seamless link between science and theology.* Everyone, please help me congratulate Dr. Madison!"

Justine, amid the tumultuous audience response, noticed Sunni Muslim cleric Abu Kalama Abdullah glaring back toward the Arabic translation booth while making urgent gestures, as if trying to cut his own throat with the edge of his hand. To Abdullah's distress, the Arabic translator was either caught up in the excitement of the moment or had chosen to ignore the imam.

Then, shouting something in Arabic, Abdullah stormed out into the atrium, enraged.

As for Rabbi Ari Feinberg, he leaned back in his chair, shaking his head in apparent consternation, perhaps grasping at last why one of the Hebrew names for God—Elohim—though designating *one* God, ends with the *plural* Hebrew suffix '-im' and why Genesis 1:26 records Elohim as saying:

Let *us* make man in *our* image [note: 'image' is singular].

Atheist Charles Stein had turned ashen pale. Across town, Becky collapsed on a hotel bed, overcome with relief and awe.

James Engle, meanwhile, walked up to Kent and hugged him, saying, "I knew there had to be some reason why I kept wanting to pull strings to get you included here. Perceiving God as the Value Continuum enables me to believe everything you have ever said about him. And by the way, I'll thank you not to gloat."

Kent hugged James back with a "Not to worry, Bro. I won't gloat but I may just wear a very wide grin."

SUBSEQUENT IMPLICATIONS

"And now, at last," Kaidan exclaimed, "following all that I teach from physical science, Dr. Madison has helped me introduce the One for whom no finite introduction can ever be adequate.

"Speaking for the 24-planet Federation, I suggest it is appropriate at last to add another name for God to your terra-lexicons. The new name I suggest is **Valcon**, a contraction of the phrase 'Value Continuum.' Using that name will help me affirm God more definitively to billions of earthlings who, often soon after childhood, choose on their own or are coerced by example to detest the idea that God may exist. I am ever so sadly aware, for that matter, that even a huge majority of Earth's intellectual elite react uneasily to any mention of God except when his name is included as part of a curse or in the context of meaningless slang.

"Be assured: trillions of inhabitants of our 24-planet Federation are more than shocked—in fact, they are *horrified*—knowing that a majority of people on Earth disdain, if not hate, the very One who forms the DNA of every living entity, the very One who—out of his *infinite* capacity to think, feel and will—imparts to us our *finite* capacities to think, feel and will. We are also aghast at how people here tolerate the proliferation of crime, of war, of injustice, of deception that inevitably accompanies alienation from him. That is by no means acceptable as a universal *status quo*."

Kaidan paused to let his words sink in. Sink in they did. Kent's eyes brimmed with tears. James, Clyde and Homer sighed sadly. Justine buried her face in her hands. Drying his eyes, Kent looked around to see many scientists gaping slack-jawed at Kaidan. Others, realizing that insights they had acclaimed earlier were actually corollary to the existence of God as triune, wore agitated frowns. Some now even looked annoyed, as if protesting: *How dare you, Sir, spend a day seeming to endorse our firmly established academic naturalism only now to ambush us with belief in God defined as an essential corollary to something we cannot deny is real—the extent continuum.*

Justine felt sure, however, that no one, not even anyone deeply averse to religion, would follow that very angry Muslim imam out of the Symposium. Human curiosity to learn as much as possible about Arkona was still almost palpable. Surely anyone antagonized by Kaidan's theism would restrain himself at least until other important knowledge of interstellar life was acquired.

Their only other option: acquiesce, due to added insight, to God as an all-knowing, everywhere-present Value Continuum.

A door at the back of the forum swung open as Abu Kalama Abdullah reentered the Symposium silently, still glaring at the Arabic translator in his translation cubicle. Had curiosity won out over rage or had an imam of higher rank ordered him to return?

Far across the room, a scientist accepted a microphone from an aisle attendant and spoke to Kaidan with a British accent.

"Noble ambassador from Arkona," he began, "On behalf of mankind, let me first apologize to Valcon and to you for the wars, the crime, the violence, the arrogance, the deceit, the disbelief, blasphemy and narcissism which, as we all must admit, are manifest throughout our world.

"Second, let me thank Valcon publicly for sending you here to teach us despite our civilization's deplorable flaws. If some of us are slow to respond to you and to him, I hope it is only because our minds as yet are floundering under the weight of so much unexpected insight.

"However that may be, Kaidan, we humbly beg you, please continue teaching us! Surely the more we absorb from you and from Arkona's traditions, the more we will want to follow your benign example."

"Thank you, Dr. Dortmund from the United Kingdom," Kaidan whispered directly into his lapel mike. "I will indeed resume teaching as requested."

But Kaidan's teachings were no longer quite so welcome elsewhere in the world. Kent's phone buzzed, alerting him to a message from Becky.

Kent, the text said, *The bad news is that China, Russia and other Communist nations, objecting to Kaidan's affirmation of God, plus Saudi Arabia, Iran, and other Muslim nations objecting to Kaidan's validation of God as triune, are trying to jam television and radio signals bringing his teaching to viewers and listeners within their borders. The good news is that their jammers began jamming up! Thus far, Kaidan's teachings are getting through! Despite their opposition, none of the nations concerned are pulling their delegates out of the Symposium in NYC. Curiosity about Kaidan and Arkona prevails, at least to that extent.*

Kent texted back a quick "thanks" to Becky and forwarded her text to the Loop.

Chapter Thirteen
A Unified Field of Truth Unveiled

FIRST, THE *PRE*-CREATION UNIFIED FIELD

Standing tall, Kaidan announced, "With the primacy of extent and value dimensions, and the two continua with their seven sub-continua thus established, I must now introduce mankind to a series of laws known to every mature unfallen citizen elsewhere in the cosmos as **the pre-creation Unified Field.**"

William Stansfield texted the Loop: *First God as 'Valcon' and now a pre-creation Unified Field as well! Can we comprehend all this? My brain is running out of kilobytes for storage!*

James replied, *Prepare for more. A 'pre-creation Unified Field' logically implies a **post**-creation series of laws to follow.*

James, glancing across at Kent, winked as he texted, *Plus, I'm guessing my friend Kent is eager to learn how three sub-value continua correspond to Father, Son and Holy Spirit.*

Kent, also with a wink, replied, *Not to worry, pal; I think I already know.*

Meanwhile Kaidan, posting headings in a variety of fonts on all seven screens, was saying: "The pre-creation Unified Field features four 'Harmonies,' each of which has one or more laws. The first Harmony features one law which is nothing less than a *sine qua non*—without which, nothing! Hence:

I. THE HARMONY OF ENTITIES

Every entity requires a perfect number of corollaries.

"Soon you will see what makes any given number of corollaries 'perfect.' For now, observe that this first law requires every entity in the Unified Field to have at least one corollary. If even one entity is so conceptually isolated as to have no corollary, the potential for a Unified Field is shattered. If, for example, there is no Value Continuum, the extent continuum violates Harmony I. The very word 'unified' implies linked corollaries.

"Our second one-law Harmony rules *dimensions*, by far the most *basic* of all entities. In this Harmony's one law, the verb 'inhere' conveys a much deeper meaning than the more common verb 'adhere.' Things that *adhere* can be separated, whereas things that *inhere* are inseparable.

II. THE HARMONY OF DIMENSIONS

Like dimensions mutually inhere
as continua with sub-continua.

"Only two kinds of dimensions exist—three of value and four of extent. Thus mutual inherence among the three and among the four yield two continua. One is a Value Continuum with three sub-Value Continua. The other is an extent continuum with four sub-extent continua. And now, inasmuch as the second Harmony's *one* law assures two continua, the third Harmony of truth must be a Harmony that features *two* laws, one for each continuum.

III. THE HARMONY OF CONTINUA

THE LAW OF THE EXTENT CONTINUUM

The extent continuum yields its four sub-extent continua infinitely and involuntarily to the Value Continuum, thereby rendering Him eternally omnipresent in space and time.

THE LAW OF THE VALUE CONTINUUM

The omnipresent Value Continuum alters finite parts of the extent continuum finitely and voluntarily by creating not only inversely equal extent density alterations (EDAs) but also value loci.

"As I have already explained, matter and energy arise via inversely equal alterations of extent designed via the wisdom, pleasure and will of Valcon—i.e., *God*, the Value Continuum.

"But when Valcon imparts a finite measure of his three values—intellect, emotion and will—to any finite locus in the extent continuum, that favored volume of extent becomes 'a value *locus*,' i.e., a *site* within the extent continuum that is now imbued with intellect, emotion and will. That locus is thus a living 'spirit,' a 'soul,' which—when linked to a physical body—can keep pace with the motion of that body much as a spotlight can follow an actor across a stage. A value locus linked to a *brain* in that body experiences sights, sounds, etc., imparted via bodily senses.

"Valcon created extent density alterations (EDAs) sufficient for the cosmos eons ago. But his creation of new finite value loci—'souls' in Earth terminology—occurs every time an infant is conceived.

"The Law of the Value Continuum permits Valcon to create or not to create a cosmos. But if Valcon chooses to create, his own law prohibits him from creating a cosmos devoid of value loci. The point of His personal law is that creating matter and energy alone would not be a worthy endeavor. If Valcon creates matter and energy, he does so to fulfill a profound goal involving finite beings endowed with finite versions of the same capacity Valcon himself wields infinitely—*the ability to make free choices!*

"Inasmuch as three eternal sub-*Value* Continua ensue from the Harmony of Dimensions, another pre-creation harmony relates to them also. But first I must ask for your help. 'Sub-Value Continua' serves well as a definitive designation but hardly honors them as exalted Persons. Please help me, friends, by coining a title fitted to three divine Beings who—though innately invisible since they exist not in material bodies but in the realm of dimensions alone—are far more real and personable than we could ever be."

Justine Hobbs took a microphone from an aisle attendant and said, "Kaidan, inasmuch as all three divine Beings are fully dimensional, I suggest we follow the precedent you set in coining the name 'Valcon' from 'Value Continuum.' I suggest we join the first four letters of the word *person* with the last six letters of the word *dimension* to make a new word—**Persension**! That will enable us to designate all three Beings as the **Persension of Omniscience**, the **Persension of Omnisentience** and the **Persension of Omnipotence**."

Kaidan nodded, "Thank you, Dr. Hobbs." Then to the entire audience he asked, "Is Dr. Hobbs' suggestion acceptable?"

UK scholar Dr. Malcolm Dortmund called out, "Persensions it is! So moved!"

"Seconded!" James echoed, winking at Justine and Kent.

Kaidan responded, "Wonderful! And so our next Harmony can thus be called:

IV. THE HARMONY OF PERSENSIONS

THE LAW OF THE PERSENSION OF OMNISCIENCE

The Persension of Omniscience *sees value* in
Himself and in all that is subordinate to Himself
and to the Unified Field of truth.

THE LAW OF THE PERSENSION OF OMNISENTIENCE

The Persension of Omnisentience *sustains meaning*
for all that is subordinate both to the Persension of Omniscience
and to the Unified Field of truth
and that is also *delightful* to Himself.

THE LAW OF THE PERSENSION OF OMNIPOTENCE

The Persension of Omnipotence *creates* whatever is
both subordinate to the Persension of Omniscience
and delightful to the Persension of Omnisentience.

"Scrutinize the four sub-extent continua and you will see that there is no basis to rank one above the others," Kaidan continued. "Yet the laws of the three Persensions reveal an *echelon* within the Godhead. All three Persensions are equally omniscient, equally omnisentient and equally omnipotent. But despite their innate equality, they acknowledge among themselves a preferred 'order,' you might say, just as three equally capable men can agree that one of them shall act as a General, another will serve as a Colonel and the third as a Major.

"So also the three Persensions have agreed among themselves that the Persension of Omniscience, because he is the *source* of omniscience and a *recipient* of omnisentience and omnipotence, shall be called God the Father. Likewise the Persension of Omnisentience, as the *source* of omnisentience and a *recipient* of omniscience and omnipotence, agrees to be called God the Son. Finally, the Persension of Omnipotence, as the *source* of Omnipotence and a *recipient* of Omniscience and Omnisentience, agrees to be known as God the Holy Spirit.

"Now you know why there can never be disagreement or competition within the Value Continuum. But why should these sourcings be a basis for defining an echelon within the Godhead?"

Justine responded, "As a psychiatrist, when I counsel patients, I urge them to discern value first, likeability second and achievability third. Could it be that Valcon also, before he created, had to discern which of several ways of creating was wisest? Also, if alternate ways to create were equally viable, would he not narrow his choice based on what he finds is most pleasure-fulfilling? Surely following parameters such as these is preferable to creating randomly."

"Thank you, Dr. Hobbs," Kaidan rejoined, "And what you have just heard Dr. Hobbs describe is really the basis for defining God as *holy*. Because all three Persensions mutually affirm their respective places in that echelon, holiness prevails!

"And now, Dr. Madison, may I ask you to name a well-known terra-book that describes God as Three Persons who are One Person and even identifies the Three with names indicative of an inner echelon?"

"In the New Testament, God is Father, Son and Holy Spirit," Kent said.

"Thank you, Dr. Madison. And is there also a text in that book that affirms one Person among the three as the primary Activator of creation?

Kent said, "Yes, the Apostle John began his Gospel with:

"In the beginning was the Word, and the Word was with God, and the Word was God....Through him all things were made....

"Words purvey *meaning*," Kent continued. "Therefore John's phrase 'The Word' designates an ultimate meaning Purveyor. John then used that same term, 'the Word,' to designate the primary Activator of creation. In so doing, John did not credit God in his entirety but the *'part'* of God, you might say, who is known as the ultimate meaning Purveyor. Also, John's emphatic comment that *'without him* nothing was made that was made' seems to imply mutual consent offered by others involved in the process. Apparently, apart from that mutual consent, any other Person in the Godhead could have created just as easily.

"It seems John was intuiting what we have agreed to call Persensions in English!" Kent said. "John says also that the same divine 'Word' put on flesh—meaning he existed before his incarnation in flesh on this earth began. And so he lived among us and was 'full of grace and truth.' That divine 'Word' can be none other than the Persension of Omnisentience: Jesus, my Lord."

"And that divine Word is my Lord, too!" Kaidan echoed. "And now, people of Earth, by unveiling the Harmony of Dimensions with its one law, the Harmony of Continua with its two laws and the Harmony of Persensions with its three laws, I am opening to you special knowledge. What you now know about Valcon makes you more responsible before him than you were before. This is a sobering reality. It is my mission to make you even more aware and even more responsible by imparting a further body of knowledge. In honor of Valcon, Lord of all, I present:

VALCON'S *POST*-CREATION UNIFIED FIELD!

"The *post*-creation Unified Field begins with Harmony Five, an array of four laws whereby post-creation phenomena are rendered eternally compatible with what was true prior to creation.

"As you may have noticed thus far, each successive Harmony elaborates on concepts featured in its immediate predecessor. So, too, our fifth Harmony presents four ways *meaning* and *existence*, mentioned in Harmony Four's second and third laws, are combined to distinguish how Valcon, citizens, denizens and matter/energy are echeloned in the cosmos.

"Valcon grants *temporary* existence to some finite entities and *eternal* existence to others. In the category of meaning, Valcon permits some entities—within limits—to do as they please, whereas others must submit to moral law. Thus we find:

V. THE HARMONY OF EXISTENCE-MEANING ACCORDS

VALCON'S ACCORD

Valcon exists eternally with
voluntarily independent meaning.

AN ACCORD FOR CITIZENS

Citizens exist eternally with
voluntarily subordinate meaning.

AN ACCORD FOR DENIZENS

Denizens exist temporarily with
innately independent meaning.

AN ACCORD FOR EXTENT DENSITY ALTERATIONS (EDAs)

Matter and energy (EDAs) exist temporarily
with *innately subordinate* meaning.

"Eternal existence has always belonged to Valcon," Kaidan reviewed. "As a freewill Being, He had to *choose* to create the cosmos and reign over it, and that is something Valcon is omnisciently, omnisentiently and omnipotently prepared to do. Yet, as a freewill Being, Valcon *may* also choose to subordinate Himself to part of His creation if He deems it necessary.

"Note that value loci whom Valcon lovingly creates as citizens need never fear annihilation. Their existence endures forever, but the only question is—where? Citizen value loci are, however, required, as free moral agents, to honor subordinate meaning by submitting to Valcon's loving rule forever.

"Value loci created on the denizen level, conversely, innately pursue—in accord with their limited existence—whatever their instincts, desires, and abilities prompt. A lion kills a gazelle lawfully. An ape who steals from a fellow ape is not a thief. An eagle feeds on fish as prey. However, the four existence-meaning accords make one point very clear: for a citizen to exalt himself as God or to act as if he were just another denizen is a dire error.

"Moving on, the Unified Field's *sixth* Harmony makes subatomic particles, atoms, photons, magnetism and gravity conform to that same five-fold motif some of you helped me delineate earlier. But, as we will now see, that same five-fold motif applies not only in the micro-cosmos but in the macro-cosmos as well. Harmony number six is called:

VI. THE HARMONY OF EXTENT DENSITY ALTERATIONS

THE SPHERICAL VOLUME LAW

Spherical volumes will exist in the micro cosmos as inversely equal hence oppositely charged particles and in the macro cosmos as matter and antimatter domain.

THE SPHERICAL SURFACE AREA LAW

Spherical surface areas appear in the micro cosmos when nucleons and electrons form concentric shells. They also appear in the macro cosmos as the double bubble.

THE CIRCUMFERENCE LAW

Circumferences travel the micro cosmos as photons. They also appear at macro levels as 'the great attractor' and 'the great repeller' chase each other around the girths of the matter and antimatter spheres.

THE DIAMETER LAW

Diameters shall appear in the micro cosmos as magnetic fields and in the macro cosmos as the cosmic 'northern' and 'southern' magnetic poles.

THE RADIUS LAW

Radii shall exist in the micro cosmos as gravity and in the macro cosmos as reversible dark energy.

"Everything in the physical cosmos accords with these five laws. And by now you probably surmise or can guess what the first Harmony means by declaring that every entity must have a 'perfect number' of corollaries. The 'perfect number' of components needed for each successive Harmony is the number that enables that Harmony to fit the *symmetry requirement* for the Unified Field as a whole.

"Watch on-screen as I plot all seven laws of the pre-creation Unified Field's four Harmonies and then add the nine laws of the two post-creation Harmonies I have presented thus far:

HOW THE UNIFIED FIELD CONFORMS TO AN EQUILATERAL TRIANGLE

Harmony I: 1 law represented by a point: .
Harmony II: 1 law, 1 line: ____
Harmony III: 2 laws, 2 lines: ____ ____
Harmony IV: 3 laws, 3 lines: ____ ____ ____
Harmony V: 4 lines, 4 lines: ____ ____ ____ ____
Harmony VI: 5 laws, 5 lines: ____ ____ ____ ____ ____

"And how many laws will the **seventh** Harmony need to have so as to extend the same symmetry requirement for the Unified Field as a whole?" Kaidan asked.

"SIX!" at least fifty people replied.

"Six laws it is, and I will present them soon. Thus the first Harmony's requirement that every entity have a 'perfect number' of corollaries establishes both pre-creation truth and post-creation truth as a single equilateral triangle. Thus every entity in the Unified Field is fitted with precisely the number of corollaries it needs to fulfill the symmetry requirement of the field as a whole.

"Note that the law for magnetism precedes mention of the law for gravity in the Harmony of *Extent Density Alterations*. That is because magnetism began accreting matter prior to gravity's influence. And, come to think of it, what better motif for Valcon to choose than the five features of a sphere as a unifying theme for the cosmos? Here it has been all along, right under the chins of thinkers for centuries, perfectly hidden in plain sight.

"But before I proceed to add the seventh Harmony to the above potent list, we left something very important unnamed. I ask for your help in giving it a most appropriate name.

"What do you propose we should name the cosmology I offered to replace Big Bang Cosmology? Any suggestions?"

Three men stood up to respond.

"Double Bubble Cosmology!" one man suggested.

"Sphere of Origin Cosmology," urged another speaker.

William Stansfield, the third responder, offered a third choice, saying, "Inasmuch as the cosmology you bring to Earth, Kaidan, is based upon the five features of a sphere, which in turn comprise one of the Harmonies of the Unified Field, I suggest this new system be named *Harmonic Origin Cosmology*!"

Kaidan called for a vote by show of hands.

Harmonic Origin Cosmology won!

Chapter Fourteen
And Now, The Seventh Harmony

"Earlier today," Kaidan reminisced, "I unveiled the first six of the seven Harmonies of Truth beginning with the four Harmonies of the **pre-creation** Unified Field. These are, in order:

    I.   The Harmony of **Entities,**
    II.   The Harmony of **Dimensions,**
    III.   The Harmony of **Continua** and
    IV.   The Harmony of **Persensions**

Moving on to the **post-Creation** Unified Field, I presented:

    V.   The Harmony of **Existence-Meaning Accords** and
    VI.   The Harmony of **Extent Density Alterations**

Now, to complete the Unified Field, I am so pleased to present:

    VII. The Harmony of **Sovereign/Citizen Rapport**

"Choosing to create freewill citizens capable of choosing to love or reject Him, Valcon ordained *six criteria* whereby He would demonstrate His holy love for them and according to which He would *expect* them to reciprocate *their* love for Him. Hence:

VII. THE HARMONY OF SOVEREIGN-TO-CITIZEN AND CITIZEN-TO-SOVEREIGN RAPPORT

    1.   The Efficiency Ideal

    2.   The Predictability Ideal

3.   The Adaptability Ideal

4.   The Abundance Ideal

5.   The Beauty Ideal

6.   The Reward Ideal

"These six ideals of behavior," Kaidan explained, "are basic to every righteous code, from the Ten Commandments given to Moses to the teaching of Jesus and his Apostles in the New Testament. Now you know which six features of behavior enable us to fulfill Jesus' affirmation of the Ten Commandments as stated in Luke 10:27-28:

> "'…Love the Lord your God with all your heart and with all your soul and with all your strength and with all your mind'; and, 'Love your neighbor as yourself.'

"First and foremost, Valcon ordains that all six Seventh Harmony Ideals be manifest in the physical cosmos," Kaidan explained. "The laws of physics function both **efficiently** and **predictably**. Plants grow and yield fruit efficiently, predictably and **abundantly**. They also flower **beautifully**. Creatures as small as birds, ants and bees fulfill Efficiency and Predictability as they build their nests or transform pollen into honey. Yet it is also true, in ways most terrans still on Earth have yet to experience, that Valcon—altering predictability via the rules of inverse equality—causes otherwise predictable phenomena to function **adaptably** so as to meet special needs. Miracles result.

"So it happens that each successive Seventh Harmony Ideal outranks those that precede it on Harmony Seven's amazing list. Thus Adaptability may overrule Efficiency and Predictability as ideals of lower rank. So also Abundance and Beauty often preempt Efficiency by calling forth phenomena that Efficiency, on its own level, could regard as extraneous. They may even overrule Predictability and Adaptability by ordaining phenomena that the two lower Ideals, each on its own level, would produce haphazardly or without regard to generosity or aesthetics.

"Highest on the Seventh Harmony list is **Reward**. Let the righteous be encouraged and evil-doers forewarned to know that Reward is by far the highest ranking hence most *preemptive* Ideal on the Seventh Harmony list! I will say more about Reward later.

"Do you recall the fifth Harmony's four Existence-Meaning Accords? If so, now you know how we as citizen value loci are expected to utilize the gift of free will so as to manifest subordination in accord with the gift of eternal existence. We are, obviously, expected to utilize the gift of free will **in ways that comply with all six Seventh Harmony Ideals**. Unfallen citizens, having all three value dimensions rightly echeloned within, find that is what they are joyfully and abundantly able to do!

THE UNBREAKABLE BOND BETWEEN
LOVE AND FREE WILL
Versus
THE POTENTIAL FOR EVIL TO ARISE
FROM FREE WILL

"Knowing we have the option *not* to love Valcon," Kaidan explained, "ennobles our choice to love him with special meaning for Him, for us and for our peers. In fact, love cannot exist apart from free will. Ironically, neither can evil exist apart from free will. So let me explain why Valcon, wanting to be loved by beings like us—though certainly not *needing* to be loved to be complete—chose a costly option, one that would require him to confront evil.

"Please keep in mind: a Being who is omniscient cannot make himself wiser. Nor can an omnipotent Being make himself stronger. But it *is* possible for an *omnisentient* Being to increase the pleasure he already enjoys in loving and being loved by his fellow Persensions. How then can *that* pleasure be increased?

"All three Persensions desire more than the pleasure they already experience by loving and being loved by each other. Creating a fourth Persension for all Three to love and be loved by is impossible; thus their sole recourse is to create finite beings endowed with free will. Only thus can they increase their holy pleasure by loving and being loved forever!

"Valcon has chosen to create finite freewill beings who are consciously external to himself, i.e., 'made in his image.' He made that choice desiring the pleasure he knows he can derive by loving and being loved by them. He made that choice despite the risk.

"Foreknowing exactly what would occur, Valcon chose to people only our 24 planets with citizen value loci, all of whom he created with their three value dimensions—intellect, emotion and will—rightly echeloned within their value loci. However, despite knowing how overwhelmingly creation and the Unified Field validate Valcon as worthily supreme, a minority, knowing that the second existence-meaning accord prohibits their annihilation even if they rebel, *violated the privilege of being endowed with free will.*

"Making that choice inverted the echelon of the three value dimensions within them, with dire results. Will, rightly echeloned, remains subordinate to Intellect and Emotion, which in turn remain subordinate to Valcon and the Unified Field. Will in a fallen value locus finds itself able to override intellect. Asserting itself as supreme, Will in fallen value loci even reduces Intellect to the quasi-rational task of justifying arbitrariness and folly. Rightly echeloned, Emotion enjoys its subordination to Intellect. Fallen Emotion, taking orders from arbitrary Will, sources envy, hate, lust, cynicism, scorn and boredom. Deformities leading to weakness, sickness and death afflicted their physical bodies. Appalled to see every rebel become so utterly self-corrupted, we— the large majority—remained true to Valcon!

"Peopling myriad worlds only to see a similar minority rebel on planet after planet was never Valcon's intent. He chose instead to cope with *just two rebellions* so ingeniously that all rightly echeloned freewill beings thereafter would be thoroughly persuaded to decline the rebellion option forever!

"Just so you know, dimensional inversion, once effected in a value locus, cannot be reversed. Nor can fallen males procreate without transmitting that fateful inversion to their offspring.

"Foreseeing their rebellion, Valcon, rather than simply overpower the first rebels, rendered them invisibly quasi-embodied and exiled them to Planet #25, this crucible world called Earth. As quasi-embodied beings, demons cannot procreate nor can they enact evil physically no matter how vehemently they try. As long as demons are subject to these limitations, Valcon is willing to endure their affront for a season.

"Demons, by the way, are able to engage in only one activity: trying to induce humans subliminally to do evil on their behalf. Humans vary as to their subliminal willingness to collude with demons. Meanwhile, demons and colluding humans together, all unwitting, are fulfilling Valcon's hidden plan, a plan designed to forestall all future rebellions in perpetuity!

"Demons banished to Earth of course misled fledgling citizens here to abuse *their* free will; hence the **second rebellion**. Because your first parents—unlike their deceivers—sinned against minuscule knowledge, Valcon makes redemption potential for Earthlings but not for demons, inasmuch as they chose to rebel despite possessing full knowledge of the Unified Field.

"So, in no way does evil disprove Valcon's existence! Conversely, evil confirms that Valcon is determined to reach for something higher than a merely robotic universe. Incidentally, if evil never occurred, how could we be sure that our wills are truly free? Better to let evil happen, find ways to discredit it consummately with wisdom and goodness, condemn it to utter banishment and then enjoy limitless love forever.

"And so now," Kaidan transitioned, "I must explain what else happens when Unified Field citizens exploit the gift of free will by inverting the echelon God ordained for their three value dimensions. Besides violating their subordinate meaning, they also become guilty of violating Harmony Seven's six ideals. Efficiency and Predictability in fallen beings give place to disorder and impulsiveness. Adaptability and Abundance are supplanted by incorrigibility and greed. Beauty and Reward are dethroned by ugliness and injustice. How, then, does Valcon react?

7th HARMONY DEPRIVATION:
A DIRE YET MERCIFUL CONSEQUENCE OF EVIL

"As I clarify still more of the incredible portent of Harmony Seven's six Ideals, the time has come for me to reveal facts that tend to astonish you human beings. For example, as I have already intimated, not only on Arkona but also on all 24

Federation planets, we have no need for policemen, judges, prisons, hospitals, doctors, dentists, optometrists or even graveyards because no one commits a crime, no one falls sick or dies and decay does not occur in relation to citizens.

"This is because in the absence of evil, Valcon, our kind and gracious Lord, assures that the very elements within our bodies, as well as in the environment around us, at His behest, fulfill all six Seventh Harmony Ideals equally at all times by guaranteeing wellness, nurture and protection. This is known as **7th Harmony *Ministration*.**"

A Symposium participant interrupted Kaidan to ask, "So you—a citizen of Arkona who remains loyal to Valcon—are an immortal person, right? So as a being who can never die, how old might you be right now, Mr. Kaidan, in terms of our terra-years?"

"I promise to answer that question in due time, Sir," Kaidan replied, "but first I must address other matters. As I was implying: in the presence of evil, finite beings indwelt by an inverted value locus must endure a moderate form of judgment known elsewhere in the cosmos as '**7th Harmony *Deprivation*.**'

"Earthlings, subject to 7th Harmony Deprivation from birth, mistakenly assume that what they experience is a universal status quo. Instead, 7th Harmony Deprivation is simply a unique form of moderated judgment designed to give fallen beings time to rue evil and thus spare themselves from something infinitely worse, namely, **7th Harmony *Abandonment*!**

"Also, 7th Harmony Deprivation assures that all evildoers' offspring who die while still innocent—i.e., as preborns, as infants or as young children—are welcomed into Valcon's eternal kingdom even if their parents are finally excluded. As Jesus taught,

> "'Let the little children come to me... for the kingdom of heaven belongs to such as these.' [Luke 18:16]

"The *third* 7th Harmony Ideal, Adaptability, for example, is almost entirely curtailed here on Earth, leaving Ideal number *two*, Predictability, almost totally unmoderated, often with unfortunate consequences.

"Thus if a typical person indwelt by a fallen value locus—a person who cannot swim, for example—falls into deep water when help is not available, Predictability, unmoderated by Adaptability, *lets that person drown!* By the same token, any person who falls off a ladder or a precipice *predictably* plummets to the ground.

"Conversely, if an *unfallen* citizen needs to walk on water for any valid reason, Valcon, via Adaptability, simply alters a probability law that determines the surface tension of water. Thus water becomes spongy-firm under that citizen's feet. Valcon balances that temporary change with an inversely equal *decrease* in the surface tension of water elsewhere on the lake. So while a citizen steps confidently on top of the water, ducks swimming nearby have to paddle with a little extra vigor to remain as buoyant as usual. For the lake as a whole, Predictability's surface tension is unviolated.

"Via ingenious skills, human chemists, doctors, engineers, machinists and physicists find ways to exploit aspects of Predictability such that medicines, MRIs, bone and organ transplants, elevators and escalators offset some of the difficulties imposed by 7th Harmony Deprivation. All such ingenuity is approved by Valcon but nothing humans devise can compare with the blessing of full 7th Harmony Ministration.

"Earthlings who catch a mere glimpse of Adaptability in action see it as miraculous. But for citizens of Arkona, phenomena in the form of automatic provisions and protection happen almost daily. And so it will be for every Earthling who, prior to death, personally entreats Valcon for the redemption that Jesus, Son of Valcon, has made available by offering himself as a once-for-all atoning sacrifice.

"The time will come, however, when judgment followed by 'the renewing of all things' will bring Earth's current 7th Harmony Deprivation to an end. Tell us, Dr. Madison, how does Paul describe that future event in his Epistle to the Romans?"

Scanning Romans chapter 8 on his tablet, Kent summarized aloud: "Paul described our present earthly environment as *'subject to frustration'* yet yearning to be *'liberated from its bondage to decay'* on that future day when redeemed people here on Earth will have *'the glorious freedom of the children of God'* restored to them. To me, that sounds pretty much like Paul was anticipating the eventual abolition of what you, Kaidan, describe as our crucible planet's current 'Seventh Harmony Deprivation.'"

"Thank you, Dr. Madison," Kaidan said. "So! The frustrating 'bondage' Paul mentioned is precisely the *frustration* the 7th Harmony 'feels' because Valcon—due to the rampant evil here on Earth—restricts the 7th Harmony such that it cannot operate as *freely* here as it does on every other inhabited world. Yet what Paul describes as 'frustration' and 'bondage' is actually a mercy in that its presence here delays a much more formidable alternative known as 7th Harmony *Abandonment*. That delay must continue until Valcon's hidden purpose related to the cosmos at large has ripened here."

With that, Kaidan turned to post still another bold headline on all seven screens:

WHY EVEN *JESUS* HAD TO ENDURE 7th HARMONY DEPRIVATION HERE ON EARTH

"Consider your own Biblical accounts of what Jesus of Nazareth was able to do while he walked on this planet. What enabled him to heal the sick, give sight to the blind and hearing to the deaf? As a sinless Person, all Jesus had to do was ask Valcon to superimpose Adaptability over Predictability and of course healings happened! After all, restoring disabled people is a task Adaptability never gets to do among *unfallen* races.

"Of course this same Jesus could also walk on water, still a storm with a word, become invisible amid people eager to harm him and even multiply a few fish and loaves enough to feed a host! Adaptability was right there at Jesus' beck and call.

"Yet I also recall," Kaidan intoned somberly, "occasions when Jesus, on purpose, declined to avail himself of Adaptability's provision and protection. Dr. Madison, please remind us of such occasions and perhaps explain why they happened."

Taking a hand mic, Kent—summoning his memory to full alert—said, after a pause: "The New Testament mentions two occasions when Jesus was *hungry*. The first is in Matthew chapter 4:2, 3." Finding the passage, he read:

"After fasting forty days and forty nights [in the desert], he was hungry. The tempter came to him and said, 'If you are the Son of God, tell these stones to become bread.'

"That was one occasion when Jesus refused to avail himself of what I now realize (with your help, Kaidan) would simply have been Adaptability's customary providence for him—i.e., inanimate objects being turned to food that would satisfy his hunger. As for the second occasion...."

Tapping his tablet keys again, Kent read from Matthew 21:18-19:

"...on his way back to the city, he was hungry. Seeing a fig tree by the road, he went up to it but found nothing on it except leaves. Then he said to it, 'May you never bear fruit again.' Immediately the fig tree withered.

"Surmisedly," Kent went on, "if Jesus sought fruit from a tree on a planet like Arkona, where Adaptability is unimpeded, any fruitless branch would yield fruit at once! But here on Earth, whereas all four Gospels show Adaptability consistently benefitting needy people all around Jesus, they also show Adaptability *becoming less and less available to Jesus himself the closer he came to his crucifixion!*

"Contemplating these two passages in the light of the 7th Harmony's six Ideals, suddenly I realize that those Ideals—all the way from number three, Adaptability, to number six, Reward—if left fully operational in Jesus' proximity, *would have totally prevented His crucifixion!*

"For example: when certain temple guards first tried to arrest Jesus, John 18:6 reveals that an invisible force knocked them flat on the ground for their intransigence. Strangely, though, when the same guards got back on their feet and tried again, Adaptability offered no resistance! It is obvious to me now that for the crucifixion to occur, as occur it must, Adaptability had to be stymied. So, in effect, the two passages I just read show Jesus prepping himself, as it were, via two 'dry runs,' to endure the shock of something far more crushing—*three full days of complete*

7th Harmony Deprivation. Only thus could Jesus be crucified and die to atone for the sin of the world."

HOW ONE MOMENTOUS DEBT CANCELS ANOTHER

Kaidan, his eyes moistening, added, "Now you all can understand what caused Jesus to cry out on the cross, 'My God, My God, why have you *forsaken me*?' But another awesome truth is begging to be recognized right here, my friends. Dr. Madison's insight actually explains how Jesus' suffering procured *atonement* for mankind. 7th Harmony Ideals from Adaptability to Reward were legally obligated to *prevent* Jesus' arrest, to *prevent* whips from lashing his back, to *prevent* thorns from piercing his brow, to *prevent* nails from piercing his hands and feet and the spear from impaling his side. **By failing to prevent these atrocities, Harmony Seven became eternally indebted to Jesus!**

"This awesome debt that the 7th Harmony thus owes to Jesus is nothing less than the antithesis of the debt fallen humans owe to the 7th Harmony. Every time someone violates *efficient* procedure, opposes valid *norms*, refuses to *adapt* as needed, acts *selfishly*, uses facial muscles to wound instead of to heal or uplift, destroys *beauty*, or scorns rather than *rewards* goodness—and these are only a few of the very mildest forms of transgression— each such person racks up a personal debt to the 7th Harmony of the Unified Field.

"Thus when Jesus encounters heartfelt repentance on the part of someone burdened with a list of 7thHarmony violations, Jesus applies the debt the 7thHarmony owes to Him to cancel the debt that repentant person owes to the 7thHarmony. For Valcon to forgive sin apart from this special atonement would be for Valcon to violate the ultimate Ideal of the Unified Field—Reward—which translates to Recompense where evil is concerned.

"Once the debtor's debt is cancelled, God the Holy Spirit *adjoins a new and wholly upright value locus to the repentant sinner's fallen one.* Thereafter, as the reborn sinner keeps his or her center of identity tethered to that new nature, he or she finds grace to do marvelous works for God despite the potential for evil that still resides within. Believe me, events such as these happen much to the awe of other-worldly beings such as yours truly."

Facing the entire Symposium audience, Kaidan said, "Thus it happened that Jesus, by suffering 7th Harmony Abandonment as if he himself had sinned, provided a way for Valcon not only to forgive sin but also to welcome sinners back into kinship with Himself. As such, they are destined to live as citizens who honor all six Ideals of the Unified Field of Truth's 7th armony.

"Now I ask, for how long did Jesus' experience of grievous abandonment last?"

"Three days!" several people responded.

"And what happened the very moment that Adaptability was re-enabled?"

"HE ROSE FROM THE DEAD!" came the jubilant shout from at least fifty people—Kent, James, Justine, Homer and William among them.

"Take a 15-minute rest," Kaidan said and left the stage.

Chapter Fifteen
Rather Than Avoid Evil, Valcon "Takes It On"!

"To the awe of loyal citizens elsewhere," Kaidan declared when he reappeared, "God the Son, born as an Earthling, chose to undergo that incredible task described earlier. Enduring painful travail and temporary death at the hands of evil-doers, Jesus, the incarnated Persension of Omnisentience, won the moral victory over evil by securing redemption via his suffering for all Earthlings who renounce evil and ask Valcon to shelter them from judgment.

"Let me emphasize again: Valcon responds to every such supplicant by adjoining a new, uprightly-echeloned value locus to the repentant rebel's still present, still inverted value locus.

"Newly 'reborn' as a child of God, the former rebel now has *one center of identity* capable of siding with either nature—the old or the new. A single 'center of identity' in a two-nature value locus is analogous to a single 'center of gravity' in a material object determining which way it may lean.

"Myriad redeemed Earthlings, despite threats, torture, enticement, fear, grief, and martyrdom, have learned to thwart evil superbly by keeping their centers of identity attached to the new nature side of their beings! When some fail to be consistent, other Earthlings mock them as hypocrites; but the mere fact that many among you do obey God despite being tethered to and tempted by a still-present fallen nature fills us unfallen beings elsewhere with awe. In the eyes of a watching cosmos, people who follow Jesus faithfully amid the menacing darkness of this world are the truest heroes in all of time and space!

"Valcon's point is this: if beings born with an inverted value locus can see evil for what it is and reject it at any cost, what should he expect from beings created with no such disadvantage?

"Sadly, many people on Earth, even among the redeemed, see Jesus' triumph over evil on this planet as a pyrrhic victory— i.e., a victory won at such great cost that its worthwhileness is moot. People misread our Lord's moral victory on the cross as if it actually benefits only a mere pittance of mankind! They forget that *two-thirds* of everyone conceived in the wombs of human mothers over ages of time have died due to miscarriage, stillbirth, abortion or childhood mortality. Be assured: those billions of souls are all in *the presence of Jesus!*

"Another segment of mankind, numbering from around 3 to 6 percent at various times and places, are 'Jobs' for whom creation's mute yet vital witness elicits a heartfelt supplication to the Creator for mercy. They, too, find salvation because the blood atonement of Jesus—albeit Jesus *'incognito'* vis-à-vis their personal awareness—covers their repentant appeal.

"Another 10 to 15 percent of the entire total are people who repent only when the specific story of redemption and/or the Old Testament's lead-up to redemption are added to the witness of creation around them. Add these segments of humanity together and we find a total of approximately 80 percent of your race rescued! Though a majority of responsible people living here on Earth at this moment may choose to remain lost, as they are free to do, they are by no means a majority of all who have ever lived!

"Here is more good news! When a redeemed Earthling dies, Valcon annihilates his or her old nature much as one might destroy a lobster's old shell after the lobster has molted. Valcon can do this legally even in terms of the 5th Harmony inasmuch as the former rebel's center of identity *no longer resides there.* Valcon welcomes all such, rendered sinless at last, to their eternal home with 7th Harmony Ministrations abundantly restored.

"End result: the wonders of creation will no longer be Valcon's sole advocate among freewill beings cosmos-wide. All future unfallen races, awed by Christ's triumph over evil on this crucible planet, will acclaim God as worthy to receive glory, honor and praise *in perpetuity.*

"Evil—exposed as hideously ignominious via events in this world—will be spurned by citizens on all future planetary systems forever. Citizens everywhere most assuredly will unanimously love Valcon while remaining still truly free to choose!

"The gift of free will, by the way, entails the right to marry and procreate responsibly. Each time Valcon creates the first man and woman on another bio-fit world, they become privileged to initiate the peopling of that new world. Given their unfallen state, death, sickness, war and tragedy are abrogated. Childbirth is painless. The population begins to multiply.

"And now you understand why," Kaidan asserted, "in this vital Symposium, I have adhered to Valcon's precedent. I began by supplementing your knowledge of creation. But to impart that knowledge alone would have been a major disservice.

"This planet Earth, already the scene of events that every citizen in the 24-planet Federation sees as paradigm shifting, will soon become a source of awe cosmos-wide as races yet to be created hear your story. That will be an unveiling of something most of you, my listeners here and elsewhere, currently dismiss as just another ho-hum tenet of just another boring religion."

At that moment Kaidan turned and addressed Kent, saying:

"Dr. Madison, in that many academics present here and others listening worldwide are biblically illiterate, I invoke your help on their behalf. I ask you to cite for translation on these six non-English screens texts of Christian scripture that reference Valcon as fostering—right here on this uniquely crucible planet—a major insight for the future benefit of interstellar civilizations."

BIBLICAL HINTS AS TO WHAT IS PENDING

Plumbing his memory for texts he had studied and reviewed from time to time, and tapping his electronic tablet to be sure of their precise wording, Kent gripped that daunting microphone again and rose to honor Kaidan's sobering request.

"Esteemed Ambassador from Arkona, several passages come to mind. First and foremost, Paul's comments in Ephesians 1:9-10 parallel your references to a hidden plan being prepared here on Earth for a great future unveiling elsewhere. I quote:

"[God has] made known to us the **mystery** of his will according to his good pleasure which he purposed in Christ, to be put into effect when the times reach their fulfillment—to bring *unity* to all things in heaven and on earth *under Christ* [emphasis added].

"The mere fact that God had to take special long-term measures to assure 'unity' everywhere in heaven as well as here on earth implies: **1)** that free will necessarily has to exist despite its potential to be wielded in opposition to God. **2)** Paul also avers, though, that unanimous cosmos-wide accord will indeed prevail provided that **3)** a very profound, long-term matrix of persuasion has been found and is also widely deployed! Finally, **4)** Paul thus implies that Christ's provision of an atonement for duly renounced evil here on Earth is the apex of that overwhelming persuasion, as Paul further explains in this further quote:

"...having disarmed the [evil] powers and authorities, [Christ] made a public spectacle of them, *triumphing over them by the cross.* [Colossians 2:15]

"Likewise in Ephesians 3:10 Paul clarifies that Christ's victory over evil at the cross, complemented by his further victory over evil via the witness of true believers, is intended to impact living beings far beyond the confines of this one planet. He wrote:

"...that now, through the Church, the **manifold** wisdom of God should be made known *to the rulers and authorities in the heavenly realms.* [emphasis added]

"Apparently Paul recognized," Kent commented, "that something known previously as 'the *wisdom* of God' had somehow become so marvelously enhanced as to merit a new title, namely, 'the *manifold* wisdom of God.' So—

"What else needed to be made 'manifold' if not the wisdom of God expressed initially via *creation alone*? What else could enhance our appreciation for God as Creator if not the splendor of what He accomplished via redemption made available to mankind through Jesus' suffering and death at Calvary?

"Kaidan, Sir, with an insider's skill you have expanded our grasp of one of Scripture's deepest apostolic themes! One would suspect that you and the Apostles had the same Teacher."

"Indeed we do!" Kaidan interjected "Please note how closely this climactic part of my teaching parallels what Dr. Madison finds in epistles given to mankind 2,000 years ago. Yesterday I expounded the wisdom of God manifest in creation. Today I am expounding the *manifold* wisdom of God as revealed via redemption. Dr. Madison, please continue."

Kent resumed, "*And*, may I add, how different this cosmic plan is from Joseph Smith's 19th-century speculation that only qualified Mormon men and women will spend eternity populating diverse planets via prolific childbearing. Not so! You clearly show that God creates unique unfallen races in their respective planetary domains. If redeemed Earthlings appear on prospective worlds it will be only to convince unfallen races to remain unfallen, thus sparing their worlds from the horrors that pall this world.

"Surely nothing less than the history of redemptive mercy triumphing over horrendous evil here on Earth can fill the hearts and minds of unfallen races with a love for God far deeper than anything they could ever feel merely by knowing him as Creator.

A TREASURE HIDDEN IN A FIELD

"I find still another parallel text," Kent added, "in one of Jesus' more mysterious parables, the one recorded by Matthew in chapter 13 verse 44 of his gospel. That is where Jesus said:

> "'The kingdom of heaven is like treasure hidden in a field. When a man found it, he hid it again, and then in his joy went and sold all he had and bought that field.'

"I posit that the field in the parable," Kent intuited, "is the basic cosmos. The man in the parable is *God*. The treasure that God anticipates rightfully owning is a host of freewill beings that he can love and be loved by. He also foresees that due to the very nature of free will, he will have to 'pay a price' to fully 'own' that kind of treasure. Ultimately, truly owning that field will entitle him to interact forever with hosts of finite beings who, out of their own freedom of choice, will love him and respond eternally to his love for them. But first, a price has to be paid via Christ's suffering. Only thus can God rightfully own this, the ultimate treasure. The only other options would have been to settle for a cosmos filled with mere robots or simply to override free will by force.

"Surely Jesus is speaking to us of God's willingness to resort to *persuasion* accompanied by prevenient grace—even his own profoundly persuasive self-sacrifice—rather than coerce finite beings by manipulation or intimidation. Anything other than persuasion would, of course, be the antithesis of wooing a genuinely unanimous freewill response from us as finite beings.

"Fourth and last of several texts that come to mind," Kent concluded, "is Luke 10:18, where Jesus recalled a time when he:

"…saw Satan fall like lightning from heaven."

As Kent sat down, he felt the pressure of hundreds of pairs of eyes bearing down on him. Much to his relief, Kaidan said:

"This is all so true! You humans are not the only quasi-rational beings inhabiting this crucible planet. The invisible remainder consist of condemned value loci interned here to await a final incarceration. All such remain hidden from human eyes because Valcon, to keep them from procreating and performing evil deeds on their own, has rendered them quasi-embodied. The only way they can perpetrate evil is vicariously, i.e., by tempting susceptible humans in a subliminal manner.

"Humans fall under their sway, not at birth but a few years later when, one by one, they submit to temptation. Even the Apostle Paul admitted that he, while still youthfully innocent:

"…*was alive* apart from the law; but when the commandment came, sin [i.e., the fallen value locus latent within him] sprang to life and I *died*. [Romans 7:9]

"The only way to escape becoming spiritually 'dead' post-childhood is to renounce evil wholeheartedly by asking God to forgive the wrongs one has done. Forgiveness then becomes freely available through Christ's atonement. Fellowship with God ensues and lasts forever."

KAIDAN'S SPECIAL APPEAL TO MANKIND

Kaidan, eyeing the Symposium audience, asked, "Why then did Valcon flex just part of his infinite four-dimensional hyper-body, the extent continuum, to create and then separate matter from antimatter? Why did he utilize magnetic field reversals to help gravity form stars, galaxies and planets? Orbs like Arkona and Earth exist to serve as well-provisioned contexts for freewill entities whom God loves and by whom he expects to be loved.

"Let me emphasize again that we are not robots pre-programmed to love and obey him. Every citizen value locus must *choose* to love or not to love the Creator. To have that capacity for moral choice is to be fashioned 'in the image of God.'

"Awesome rewards ensue for all who love God and honor truth. Perpetual alienation awaits all who disdain God and truth.

"Apart from free will, any and every response to Valcon could be only robotic, hence meaningless both to him and to us. My ability to choose not to love Valcon is what makes my choice to love him eternally significant. That is exactly what every citizen in the 24-planet Federation chooses. If only that choice could be unanimous here on Earth as well!"

"Be sure, every rationalization, every distraction that keeps you from receiving salvation through Jesus is something that is foisted on you by none other than Valcon's enemies. Eternal peril awaits every fallen value locus who fails to avail himself of the redemption that Jesus has procured for you *at such great cost*.

"Your response to me as a teaching ambassador from far-away Arkona is deeply gratifying. It is vastly more essential, however, that you welcome Jesus Christ, second person of the Godhead, as your Savior and Lord. The entire citizenry of the 24-planet Federation has commissioned me not only to add to your knowledge of the physical cosmos, but also to plead with you to join us as citizens of Valcon's cosmos-wide kingdom.

"In fact, I plead here and now with everyone seated in this forum and worldwide who has not yet sought Valcon's forgiveness to rise to your feet as a sign of your commitment to be a true follower of Jesus Christ, Son of God, from this day onward!"

James Engle was the first to rise, followed by Justine Hobbs, Homer Grassley, William Stanfield and, moments later, by Clyde Smith. But Charles Stein, Ari Feinberg, Abu Kalama Abdullah, the other Muslim imam, the Hindu and Buddhist priests and many other attendees remained seated. Almost 200 people had risen in response, many with heads bowed.

Virtually every cameraman, meanwhile, swiveled his lens from Kaidan to the many responders and from them to the still-seated majority. What were so many august personalities, elite by Earth standards, thinking? Kent saw many sitting stiffly, deep in thought. Others exhibited frowns, indicating that they regarded Kaidan's appeal as an unwelcome intrusion. Here and there, floodlights caught a gleam of tears glistening on an eyelid.

"I call on Dr. Kent Madison, a man who faithfully teaches the message of Christ," Kaidan continued, "this time to help responders verbalize a prayer beseeching Jesus to redeem you."

Phrase by phrase, Kent led everyone standing in the forum and perhaps millions worldwide in supplicating God for salvation with a simple prayer. When he finished, James walked straight over to Kent and asked, "Where can I get an electronic Bible like the one you have in your tablet? I can see I've got reams of catching up to do."

"Great idea, Bro!" Kent replied. You can find electronic versions of the Bible—some free, some for sale—on the Web for your phone, tablet, laptop, or all three! Most websites selling Christian materials sell electronic Bibles. After this session, let me show you the version I have."

Kent texted Becky: "James is now our brother in faith."

"I'm sure many of you would like to ask me a question or two," Kaidan understated with a grin. "Who wants to be first?"

A QUESTION FROM A DOUBTER

One questioner summoned the courage to ask, "Kaidan, replying to your requests, Dr. Madison keeps finding biblical parallels to your theology. But surely, Sir, it must concern you that other teachings in the Bible contradict your cosmology. The Book of Genesis, for example, claims that Valcon completed the creation of the heavens and the Earth a mere 6,000 years ago and even accomplished the entire task within the span of a mere six days. How do you respond?"

"I'm glad you asked!" Kaidan replied. "Actually, the Genesis account of creation reads like a Hebrew translation of a much more ancient Arkonan text—except that our text uses cosmological terminology for which the Hebrew language at that same time had little more than approximations. As an example, where your English translation of the Hebrew text of Genesis 1:2 says that:

"…darkness was over the surface of the deep, and the Spirit of God was hovering over the waters…,

our text in Arkona reads: **'The extent continuum was still in a state of zero energy with Valcon omnipresent in all four sub-extent continua.'**

"Genesis 1:3-5 in a popular version of the English Bible known as the New International Version (NIV), continues:

"And God said, 'Let there be light…and he separated the light from the darkness. God called the light 'day' and the darkness he called 'night.' And there was evening, and there was morning—the first Day.'

"Arkona's account, however, reads: **'Amid a continuum that had never known creation, Valcon chose to create. Valcon formed creation in the midst of non-creation—a transition from peaceful 'night' to glorious 'day.'**

"So also the Hebrew text of Genesis 1:6-7 has God saying:

"'Let there be a vault between the waters to separate water from water.' So God made the vault and separated the water under the vault from the water above it.

"The Hebrew word translated in the NIV as 'vault'—*raqiya*'—designates the *arch* of the sky above the earth. Thus *raqiya*' refers not to a *flat* expanse, as people tend to suppose, but to a domed expanse which, if traced 360 degrees in all directions around the globe, is found to be a *sphere*!

"Earlier versions of this same popular English translation rendered *raqiya*' simply as 'expanse' instead of 'vault.' 'Vault' is indeed much more consistent with the idea of curvature conveyed by the Hebrew word 'raqiya."

James, Kent and Homer saw at once how closely Genesis 1:6-7 parallels Harmonic Origin Cosmology. James thought, *As a scientist I feel so rebuked by what I now see in these amazing texts.*

Kaidan, as if reading James' mind, looked straight at him and said: "How fitting, then, that our parallel text on Arkona reads: **'So Valcon, after selecting a site for a *sphere of origin*, separated a plasma of matter *inside* the sphere from a plasma of antimatter *outside* the sphere.'**

"How else could a Hebrew sage ages ago render 'plasmas' other than to call them 'waters'? The Hebrew word is *'mayim,'* which means not only H_2O but virtually any liquid.

"Thus I feel quite at home with the Genesis account of creation. I know many good people devoutly believe that the seven 'days' of creation were actual 24-hour periods, but we in Arkona understand them to have been *eras*.

"Indeed, the Hebrew word *'yôm,'* translated as 'day' in Genesis 1, has a dozen or so meanings and usages in Scripture, one of which is a 24-hour period. Others meanings are a 'time,' a 'period,' and a 'year.' Its usage in Psalm 90:4 reveals a poetic propensity to use brief spans of time—a 'yesterday' or a 'watch in the night'—to designate a millennium, for example.

"The 'era' interpretation is verified in that chapter 1 of Genesis says in relation to each of the first six days, 'And there *was* evening and there *was* morning....' But it does *not* describe the seventh day as already ended, past tense. That is because we are still experiencing God's seventh day of rest, as the writer of the New Testament letter to the Hebrews attests.

"I revere these texts, as do all citizens in the 24-planet Federation. It amazes us that many on Earth ignore them."

Silence ensued. Kent was not in the least surprised that scientists needed time to accommodate so unexpected a perspective on Genesis chapter 1.

WAS THE COSMOS CREATED *EX NIHILO?*

Another participant rose to his feet and questioned, "Mr. Kaidan, you make a very clear case that matter and energy are nothing more than four-dimensional extent altered in various inversely equal ways. That premise conflicts with a longstanding tenet of Judeo-Christian theology that posits God as creating everything *ex nihilo*, meaning 'out of nothing.' Thus I am curious to know if Dr. Madison, as a Christian theologian, takes issue with you on that question."

"What say you, Dr. Madison?" Kaidan asked.

Kent replied, "I myself used to believe that creation happened *ex nihilo*—that is, "out of nothing"—until I noticed that the author of the letter to the Hebrews stated in chapter 11 verse 3 that God has made what is *seen*, not out of *nothing* but out of *something invisible*. The wording in my English translation is, 'what is seen was not made out of what was visible.' The Greek language has words for 'nothing' that the author of Hebrews could have chosen if that were his intended meaning, but he did not. An invisible *something* does not equate to *nothing*-ness. Clearly God used an already-existing something to create the cosmos. Originally homogeneous extent, as you emphasize, Kaidan, was a totally *invisible* something from which the Value Continuum—via inversely equal alterations—gave rise to visible matter and energy in all its manifestations.

"Theologians who, ages ago, began propagating the tenet that God created the cosmos 'out of nothing' were most likely thinking of empty space as *nothing*. If so, they were unwittingly affirming your present-day explanation of creation. Little did those long-ago thinkers know that a 'void' or a 'vacuum' is actually space-time, the ultimate opposite of physical nothingness.

"To describe God as existing *before* time and *outside* of space is utterly meaningless. The word 'before' is a time indicator; hence 'before' cannot be used to describe an absence of the very thing that gives it meaning! Likewise, 'outside,' as a space indicator, has no meaning apart from space; hence 'outside' cannot be used to designate a total absence of the very thing that gives it meaning. This heard-everywhere self-contradiction compounds enormously when the same people who use it also describe God as having existed *'from eternity past,'* a statement that credits time as having no beginning!

"Consider also that finite and infinite dimensions can not be joined within the same continuum. Thus if time denotes infinite duration, the other three extent dimensions must also be infinite. In short, the extent continuum cannot be part of creation at all. Rather, as Kaidan explained earlier, it is the infinite *source* whereby Valcon created everything finite via inversely equal 'extent density alterations.' I expect it will not be long before the *'ex nihilo'* approach to the origin of the cosmos will be abandoned throughout Judeo-Christian theology," Kent concluded.

"It is already being replaced," Kaidan said assuredly. "And now, do I have a further question from among you?"

Kent felt tension rising everywhere in the forum as a formidably renowned geologist, microphone in hand, challenged Kaidan to confirm terra-geology's conviction that the Genesis Flood never happened.

Chapter Sixteen
A Geologist Objects to Noah's Flood

Dr. Rolf Jorgensen, microphone in hand, challenged Kaidan in front of the Symposium audience and the world. "Esteemed visitor," he began, "my colleagues in astrophysics, cosmology and subatomic physics seem impressed by your insights relative to their respective realms of study. I think we are also intrigued by your view of the author of Genesis—Moses or whoever—despite the limited lexicon of his era, bravely translating a valid text that exists on Arkona and, incidentally, getting it marvelously correct for a man of his time.

"Further along in Genesis, however, we have the story of a worldwide flood. Since it seems you are eager to credit the Bible as true, some of my fellow geologists are texting me to ask, and I myself want to ask, do you also affirm the Genesis Flood as historical? If you reply 'Yes,' our next question is, 'Where did all that excess water come from, Sir,' and finally, 'Where is all that excess water *now*?'

"Our point is, if the entire Earth was deluged at any time in the past, it should still be deluged *now*. That much excess water could not simply ebb away somewhere, like a tide ebbing away due to the gravity of the moon."

KAIDAN RESPONDS

Kaidan, squaring his shoulders, responded, "Before I answer all three right-to-the-point questions, Doctor Jorgensen, I want to make a statement and then ask you to evaluate that statement for everyone. My statement is simply to say that **this planet we are standing on—Earth—has only two really major**

mountain ranges. I ask you, Doctor, to clarify if that statement is true or naively wrong."

Jorgensen, taken aback and sensing a possible set-up, hesitated momentarily. Then, throwing caution to the winds lest he be thought not up on his science, he averred with confidence, "I'm sure you yourself know that your statement is naively wrong, Sir. The Earth has more than two dozen VERY significant mountain ranges. But why even ask if such a statement could be valid?"

"It is a true statement, Doctor, as I will now clarify."

Using his remote, Kaidan filled all seven screens with a full-color map of the Pacific Ocean. "One of Earth's two major mountain ranges, Dr. Jorgensen," Kaidan explained, "is the **Ring of Fire** surrounding the Pacific. It includes the **Aleutian volcanoes**, North America's **Coast Range** and the **Rockies**, Central America's **Sierra Madre**, the **Andes**, Antarctica's **Hinson Massif**, the **Southern Alps** in New Zealand and the 1500-mile-long **Maoke** mountain range of New Guinea, the central mountains of the Philippines, Formosa, and Japan, and the high peaks of Russia's Kamchatka Peninsula."

Each range popped up in red as Kaidan named it.

"Yes, I see, of course," Jorgensen replied. "Viewing all these ranges as one extensive system makes a valid point. But what is the other single system that you suggest ranks on a par with the Pacific Ocean's Ring of Fire?"

Clicking his remote again, Kaidan filled all seven screens with charts including Europe and all of southern Asia.

"The Ring of Fire is roughly circular," Kaidan responded, "but the counterpart of the Pacific Ocean's Ring of Fire is a **roughly straight-line mountainous system** stretching from west to east across southern Europe and Central Asia. Beginning with the **Pyrenees** in northern Spain, this second major system continues with the Swiss and Italian **Alps**, the **Carpathians**, the **Caucasus**, the **Elburz**, the **Pamirs**, the **Karakorum**, the **Hindu Kush**, the **Kunlun**, the **Himalayas** and the **Tibetan plateau!**"

Again, each successive range, as if awakened by the sound of Kaidan's voice, popped up in red on the seven maps. The entire Symposium audience murmured with awe. Kaidan continued.

"My friends on Earth, earlier today I introduced you to the Value Continuum—the ultimate missing corollary of the extent continuum. Now I claim the privilege of focusing your attention upon the **Trans-Eurasian Cordillera**, which is nothing less than a *straight-line* missing corollary to Earth's *circular* Ring of Fire!"

A flustered Jorgensen, rather than admit that Kaidan had outfoxed him at his own game, simply muttered, "Proceed, Sir."

"This straight-line Trans-Eurasian Cordillera," Kaidan continued, "beginning most noticeably with the Caucasus in Central Asia, features **ever-loftier summits sprouting above a base that keeps widening its girth extensively as we track it eastward**. This trend, accompanied by a slight southeasterly turn at the end, culminates of course with the Tibetan plateau. Flanked by the Himalayas to the south and the Kunlun Mountains along its northern edge, the Tibetan plateau is a vast region where scarcely any terrain dips below 10,000 feet above sea level.

"Surely this base, massively widening its girth under summits that rise higher the further east we go, bears witness to the aftermath of a very special force. That force, relatively weak while uplifting the *western* end of the cordillera in question, became increasingly more powerful while uplifting first the *central* and then the *eastern* sectors of the same system.

"More amazing than the fact that the **Trans-Eurasian Cordillera** and the **Ring of Fire** exist at all is the fact that these two systems are oriented such that one range marks the **onset** of a certain cataclysmic event whereas the other range represents the **aftermath** of that same event! To explain, let me first expand the Pacific basin back to the much wider parameters it had when all the continents were conjoined as a single land mass that Terra-geologists dub as 'Pangaea.'"

Next, Kaidan displayed on-screen the entire world prior to continental drift. **North** and **South America** were aligned with the west coast of Europe and Africa. **Australia**, with **New Zealand** abreast, rested next to East Africa. **India** was a triangle wedged between Australia and Arabia. **Antarctica**, prior to slipping away to rest atop the South Pole, abutted South Africa. All of these adjoined land masses were colored green.

"According to terra-geology, as surely as all the continents were one," Kaidan resumed, "at that time all the oceans had to be one as well. Thus the Pacific, Atlantic and Indian Oceans, all conjoined in that era, accounted for some 60 percent of the Earth's surface. Let me call it the 'multi-ocean expanse.'"

Arcing his remote, Kaidan drew a straight black line across what—following the breakup of Pangaea—would be known as southern Eurasia. Next, Kaidan extended that black line with a slight southeasterly curve out across the blue-colored 'multi-ocean expanse.' At length that black line ever so neatly crossed the multi-ocean expanse to its very center, which of course was also destined to become the center of the Ring of Fire!

"So!" Kaidan summarized, "Earth's two truly major mountain ranges are oriented as follows: Eurasia's roughly straight-line mountain range points toward the center of the Pacific Ocean's circular mountain range in terms of where that center was located prior to continental drift. Thus I conclude that the force that kept widening and heightening the Trans-Eurasian range is the same force that somehow uplifted an originally longer yet still roughly circular Ring of Fire."

Almost everyone in the forum already knew about terra-geology's popular diagrams of "Pangaea," a single land mass which, eons ago, broke apart to form Earth's various continents. That said, Kaidan's next comment startled everyone.

"The single force terra-geology credits as causing Pangaea to break apart," Kaidan reviewed, "is sub-crustal convection currents that keep lava churning deep down in Earth's mantle. That churning alone, however, cannot account for the steadily increasing width and uplift of the Trans-Eurasian Cordillera *and* its special orientation to the Pacific Ocean's Ring of Fire. Only one other force can account for the origin of both ranges in the context of continental drift.

"It was by no means a force from *below*," Kaidan intoned. "Rather it was a force from *above*, as I will now explain."

Holding his remote aloft, Kaidan pressed down on a control. Before a rapt worldwide audience, virtually the entire blue area representing the expanse of what terra-geology surmises was Earth's long ago 'pan-ocean' **suddenly changed from blue to**

green with blue dots—relatively small masses of water—replacing a single massive expanse of ocean.

WHAT A DIFFERENT WORLD THIS PLANET WAS!

"Prior to the cataclysmic event that brought forth both the Trans-Eurasian Cordillera and the Ring of Fire," Kaidan continued, "Pangaea was much larger than just the present continents conjoined. The entire Earth was Pangaea! Yes, there were numerous large salty seas, many lakes, countless ridges, rills and hills but no oceans and no lofty mountain ranges. Minimal evaporation due to the absence of oceans precluded rain and hurricanes and, as a result, no one ever saw a rainbow either. However, high humidity, heavy dew and a worldwide just-below-the-surface water table assured adequate moisture for flora, fauna and for humans.

"Also, because the axis of the earth was rotating virtually at right angles to the ecliptic at that time, seasons were an unknown phenomenon. Even in what is now **Siberia**, luxuriant vegetation—fostered by continuous sunshine beaming in just above a night-less polar horizon—sustained beasts as large as **mammoths**, none of whom could survive there today!

"That was all about to be changed, as I will explain next."

On-screen maps gave place to a scene above the Earth in space as Kaidan continued narrating.

"A huge comet (let me name it 'Comet X'), while on its way toward the Sun, approached Earth. Comet X had a massive, pear-shaped iron head pulling a tail consisting mainly of several million cubic miles of water, meteoroids and nitrogen gas. Small end first, the head of Comet X came arcing in over what is now Spain. While still more than 3,000 miles above Earth and spinning on its axis, Comet X's gravity uplifted the Pyrenees.

"Turning its larger end Earthward while being pulled in closer by the reciprocal attraction of Earth's gravity, the spinning iron projectile uplifted the Alps more forcefully and the Carpathians with a little less gravitational force.

"Soon that oddly ovoid mass, arcing still closer, presented its larger end over what is now the eastern area of Turkey. That is when its gravity, in quick succession, uplifted the Caucasus, Pamirs, Elburz, Karakoram, Hindu Kush ranges and of course the Tibetan plateau.

"East of the Tibetan plateau, Comet X's gravity became so strong as to do more than merely raise mass up *on* the earth's surface. It began lifting mass up *from* Earth's surface only to let some of the mass it uplifted drop back into place at oddly steep angles. That is how Comet X contributed to the formation of strikingly sheer mountains in the Wulingyuan region of what is now southwestern China.

"Soon the sudden uplift and subsequent release of an enormous cordillera of towering ranges imposed enormous pressure on water trapped in subterranean caverns. That water, gushing up to the surface, merged with artesian flows ensuing from the tilt-up of a water table that, in enormous areas, *was suddenly no longer horizontal.*

"That is why it was recorded in the seventh chapter of Genesis that 'all the springs of the great deep burst forth.' Much greater amounts of water, however, were yet to 'come upon' the Earth when 'the floodgates of the heavens were opened,' as I will soon explain.

"Moments later, however, the effect of the comet's *gravity* upon Earth was about to be enormously surpassed by the impact of *Comet X itself* as its mass collided with Earth!

55% OF EARTH'S CRUST—PEELED AWAY LIKE THE RIND OF A NAVEL ORANGE

"The leading edge of X's head, like a 4000-mile-long blade of an interstellar planet peeler, plunged under the crust of the Earth beginning in what is now the western Pacific Ocean between New Guinea and Japan. Its foremost rocky prong gouged out the deepest hole anywhere on Earth's crust—the Mariana Trench, which is still 1500-miles long with depths ranging from five miles to a maximum of seven miles in what is known as the Challenger Deep.

"Pushing east by southeast at close to 25,000 miles per hour, Comet X began surgically separating a widening expanse of 20-mile-thick solid crust away from Earth's underlying liquid mantle. Just as wedging one's thumb under the rind of a navel orange enables one to remove much more of the rind than is actually in contact with one's thumb, so also Comet X began uplifting sections of Earth's crust thousands of miles away from the main impact.

"But, as Comet X gouged still deeper between Earth's crust and the underlying liquid mantle, the shock of its impact plus the force of Earth's stronger gravity split Comet X into at least two major masses of iron. Now there were at least two 'thumbs' severing the 'rind' of the 'navel orange' from the 'fruit.'

"One mass continued gouging east and slightly southeast toward the part of the crust that would later separate from Pangaea as 'North America.' The other main mass veered more acutely southeast toward the part of the crust that would later separate as 'South America.' Between them they and lesser fragments of the head of Comet X peeled away slightly more than half the surface of the Earth in less than two minutes!

"Still, the invader's unstoppable momentum—abetted by Earth's own gravity—was yet to mar Earth even more savagely by bulldozing twin cavities into Earth's liquid mantle itself. Soon these cavities became several hundred miles deep in what is now the center of the eastern Pacific Ocean.

THE DIFFERENCE BETWEEN A SPLASH AND AN ENSUING WAVE

"How then did the Ring of Fire—circular corollary of the by-then already upraised straight-line Trans-Eurasian Cordillera— come into existence? It was already there as a prototype of what was yet to be!" Kaidan announced.

"The upraised edge encompassing the great abyss where Comet X's two splintered masses had robbed Earth of crust (and even left it bereft of magma down to depths of several hundred miles in some places) consisted of crust that was left up-tilted but not torn away.

"One part of that Great Rim—a part destined to be known as North America's Coast Range—was uplifted as Comet X's northern 'thumb' was already rebounding away from Earth. Yet that part of Comet X, while still impacting Earth, had already caused a deeper west-to-east surge in Earth's liquid mantle prior to rebounding away. East of what is now the Coast Range, that deeper surge began uplifting a series of bulges separated by wider and wider gaps across what is now North America.

"First and nearest to the Coast Range, a parallel uplift became known as 'the Selkirks,' and the 'Cascades' immediately south of it and the 'Sierra Nevada' at its southernmost end. Further east, an even stronger upwelling crested as the Rocky Mountains, where hot geysers still gush in places. Losing strength, the underlying force left an even wider gap before uplifting the Appalachians.

"Throwing a rock into still water creates two byproducts: a splash and a series of waves. View the Coast Range as part of Comet X's *splash*. Parallel ranges separated by consecutively wider gaps further east mark successive crests of ensuing sub-crustal waves.

"By that time Comet X's powerful impact had also tilted Earth's axis over to its present-day angle relative to the ecliptic.

THE ORIGIN OF DOZENS OF
LESSER MOUNTAIN RANGES

"Thus it happened: the two parts of Comet X's head, leaving an upraised rim around a vast abysmal ocean of red-hot lava, proceeded to accelerate and scatter millions of cubic miles of crust mixed with underlying magma into outer space. Parts of that mass, reaching speeds greater than escape velocity, accreted gravitationally to the surface of Comet X. Other parts—pushed aside by segments of Comet X or simply lagging behind them—fell back upon still intact parts of the Earth to form lesser mountain clusters and ranges.

"The Great Rim—left towering raggedly above what mankind would later define as 'sea level'—was destined eventually to break apart into the lengthy segments that comprise planet Earth's present-day *Ring of Fire*. But before that great segmentation occurred, the Great Rim fulfilled a singularly different initial purpose. That Great Rim first had to serve as a 20,000-mile long dam! And why would that be?

A 20,000-MILE-LONG SEA WALL

"Planet Earth had indeed 'lost face' due to Comet X's devastating 'hit and run,' but now Earth was in a position to avenge itself royally on Comet X. Earth now stood squarely between Comet X and Comet X's million-mile-long tail. Drawn in by Earth's gravity, enormous swashes of Comet X's watery tail began spiraling in toward Earth from all directions. Rain cascading everywhere on the still-intact 45 percent of Earth's surface soon progressed from pooling to flooding. Contained initially by that 20,000-mile-long upraised rim, water soon deepened above treetop level and up to even more than a mile above that.

"Rain falling in torrents on mountains of mixed crust and magma served to cool semi-liquid magma such that it hardened in place. Loose soil and rock, washed down by intense rain, formed foothills around such masses, making mountains newly fallen from the sky look like peaks that had been situated there for ages. In some places, weighty masses of rock smashed down upon the crust of Earth hard enough to open fissures through which lava eventually gushed, transforming newly emplaced mountains into erupting volcanoes!

"Rain falling nonstop on Earth's newly de-crusted side found half a globe of molten lava eager to boil it back into the sky as clouds of steam. Much of the steam, billowing around to the still intact side of Earth, cooled enough to precipitate as rain on that side of the planet, thus adding to the deluge rising steadily between the walls of the 20,000-mile-long dam formed by the Great Rim.

"At last, after about a fortnight of continuous downpour, liquid water prevailed over molten lava even on Earth's disrupted face. The upper meter or so of magma cooled and even solidified enough for water to collect. Rivers of hot water, flowing downhill from all directions, began filling the lowest depressions of the lava-scape with the beginnings of Earth's soon-to-be multi-ocean!

"And still the rain continued cascading from extremely dark skies over every quarter of Earth.

"Friends, consider with me the situation that existed. Forty-five percent of Earth—Pangaea, if you will—still had a twenty-mile thick solid crust plus the added weight of a million or so cubic miles of water walled in place by the Great Rim. And all of this mass was resting down upon liquid magma that was rather highly elevated relative to the crust-less and partially excavated magma on Earth's disrupted side.

"Inches-per-year convection currents in Earth's mantle," Kaidan called aloud, "had absolutely nothing to do with what happened next. Just as water, apart from absorption, seeks its lowest level, so too does liquid magma. Gravity, via magma's ability to flow, strives to preserve planet Earth as much as possible in the shape of a sphere. Hence natural law required that the depressed 55 percent of the planet be elevated as close as possible back to where it had been. To that end, liquid magma began to flow out from under Pangaea in all directions.

CONTINENTS—A GEOLOGICAL ARMADA— LAUNCHED!

"As the underlying magma flow gained momentum, sections of Pangaea snapped apart only to be borne away in diverging directions. Also, segments of the Great Upraised Rim broke apart, allowing water to cascade with incredible force via widening gaps in the Rim. Some sections of the wall became so eroded that they simply crumbled.

"For its part, Antarctica broke away on a southerly Great Circle Route toward the center of the multi-ocean, a route that would eventually leave it stalled over the South Pole. There it would begin amassing layers of ice that are now two miles high.

"Australia launched eastward, leaving Africa far behind and even trailing a wake of Indonesian islands on its bow side. New Zealand, bearing part of the Great Wall, broke off ahead, leading Australia along like a tugboat pulling a huge vessel. Initially, India also glided eastward until suction created in the underlying magma by the uplift of the Tibetan Plateau swept India northeastward. India crashed against the Tibetan plateau's southern edge, forcing up the Himalayas even higher.

"North and South America, breaking away as one from Europe and Africa, took the longest single segment of the Great Rim with them. Yes, Plato was correct: something called 'Atlantis' did indeed rumble away from Europe and vanish beyond the western horizon.

"So, Dr. Jorgensen, you asked me where all the excess water came from? I reply that it came from the tail of Comet X! Where did all that excess water go? It is all still with us, Doctor. As Antarctica, India and Australia separated from Africa, part of the water that had inundated all of Pangaea filled the widening gap they left behind them, hence the origin of the *Indian* Ocean. As North and South America separated from the western side of Europe and Africa, some of the water that had inundated all of Pangaea filled the widening gap *they* left behind, hence the origin of the *Atlantic* Ocean.

"The rest of the water flooding Pangaea, gushing out via widening gaps in the Great Rim, rushed ahead of Earth's newly launched armada of drifting continents. Joining the greater part of the water harvested from Comet X's tail, both bodies merged to inundate the major part of the vast lava-scape Comet X left behind—the floor of the Pacific Ocean.

"Though continental drift began slowly, within a matter of days it had accelerated to several kilometers per hour. By the time the Great Magma Flow, coming in from all sides, had elevated the Great Pacific Depression back to within two miles of where the surface of pre-flood Earth had been, continental drift had slowed to its present rate of inches per year.

"Evidence that North America's continental drift briefly attained a speed of several kilometers per hour has been found in rock cores taken from ancient lava flows in eastern Oregon. When lava stops flowing, iron atoms in the lava uniformly orient their tiny poles in relation to Earth's magnetic field. Then, as a lava flow hardens from top to bottom, iron atoms lose their ability to shift their magnetic orientation. Ergo, iron atoms in core samples taken ages later ought to show the same orientation throughout each entire core from end to end.

"Surprisingly, the magnetic orientation of iron atoms at opposite ends of the Oregon rock cores vary by as much as **sixteen** *degrees*! To induce that great a shift of orientation, North America—during the month or two the lava took to cool from top to bottom—had to be moving from east to west at one or two kilometers per hour relative to Earth's north magnetic pole.

"If rock cores are drawn from *ancient* lava in New Zealand, Australia and New Guinea, top to bottom iron-atom orientation predictably will show a west to east drift rather than an *east to west* motion, as in Oregon. Iron in cores drawn from lava in Antarctica will show *zero* shift due to that continent's *north to south* drift.

"Terrans, the Great Flood and the major part of continental drift happened concurrently!" Kaidan exclaimed. "As stated in Genesis 7:11 and 8:14, Noah and kin remained in the Ark one year plus 10 days. By then, continental drift had slowed to a negligible rate and land surfaces were reasonably dry. Antarctica and Greenland, of course, were already beginning to amass ice

"A lesser meteorite impact near Yucatan had already pushed the dinosaurs to extinction, but only the Genesis comet/Flood event could expose thousands of feet of rock strata and render massive oil and mineral deposits accessible to mankind.

"I can describe Earth's Flood in this much detail because Valcon assigned some of my fellow citizens to stow thousands of varieties of flora and fauna from various sectors of Earth in their spaceships and/or drop species off near the Ark while everyone slept! Arkonans also lingered nearby in space to shuttle many species back to their appropriate locations afterward. Hosts of land-based species were thus spared from extinction. I know this having read fascinating reports annotated by my fellow-citizens.

"Believe me, Dr. Jorgensen, Earth's flood event became major news on all 24 Federation worlds!"

Almost the entire audience stood to its feet with a roar of applause. Jorgensen, visibly shaken, slumped down in his seat.

WHY ARCTIC MAMMOTHS FROZE SO QUICKLY

"I do have just one more terra-mystery to solve for you while I'm still on the subject of the Flood," Kaidan added. "It has to do with mammoths that once roamed amid luxuriant vegetation in what is now frigid northern Siberia. Those same long-ago visitors from Arkona, by the way, were under orders not to try to spare mammoths. The condition attached to mammoth existence was expiring. Exactly how, then, did Siberian mammoths perish?

"As I'm sure many of you know, mammoths have been found preserved in Siberian ice. Inasmuch as Siberia's climate was pleasant back in their day, the mystery is—what could have frozen such huge beasts so suddenly that food they had just swallowed froze while still undigested in their big warm bellies?

"There is only one answer. What did I tell you was intermixed with water and meteoroids in Comet X's tail? *Nitrogen!* Whereas nitrogen exposed to the sun in exterior parts of X's tail was a gas, nitrogen deep inside the tail was still as cold as it had been journeying far out beyond Pluto. In other words, nitrogen deep inside Comet X's tail was still in *liquid* form.

"As surely as Comet X's tail neared Earth over northerly latitudes, liquid nitrogen from Comet X's tail deluged Siberia. Entering the mammoths via their mouths and nostrils, it froze them instantly to the very core of their huge bodies. Within hours, all the liquid nitrogen that smothered and froze the mammoths evaporated to join nitrogen that was already part of Earth's atmosphere. Frozen water kept the mammoths preserved, but ice alone could not have accomplished that initial deep-freeze.

"So now you know, people of Earth, why the Pacific Ocean is so much larger and is on average twice as deep as Earth's other oceans and is also the only ocean encompassed by a Ring of Fire. Now you also know why several thousand aboriginal traditions that attest to a Great Flood have merit.

"Comet X caused great destruction and loss of life and it is still the long-ago cause of most of today's earthquakes and hurricanes. But it was not without some benefit. By upraising entire cordilleras and lesser mountains, it rendered precious metals and ores of iron, copper and other metals, plus deposits of oil, much more accessible for mankind's future needs."

Most Symposium participants sat agog. As for geologist Jorgensen, he simply folded his arms in apparent resignation.

An archaeologist too eager to wait for a microphone called aloud to ask Kaidan, "Where can we find ruins or relics left by that long-ago pre-flood civilization?"

Another asked, "What of the people alive back then, Kaidan? Was the Flood a tragic accident or is it true that mankind merited punishment? And if the Flood was indeed a punishment, which crimes were so utterly evil as to merit *that*?"

Kaidan responded, "Sirs, I will answer the questions you both raised, in the order you asked them."

Chapter Seventeen
Seven Evocative Pre-Flood Symbols

"In response to the gentleman's desire to search for ruins and relics left by the pre-Flood civilization," Kaidan began, "I am sad to say that extremely turbulent currents and landslides buried or destroyed nearly everything in their domain—an area centered west of what is now the Black Sea. What *did* survive from that ancient era are mainly *symbols* memorializing the 22 laws of the Unified Field. When finally that society rebelled, the fact that they rebelled despite full knowledge of the Unified Field intensified Valcon's reaction. Though insights represented by those ancient symbols vanished ages ago from human comprehension, Flood survivors at least preserved symbolic representations of what had originally been known and held in awe.

"For example, people in the pre-Flood civilization represented the three Persensions of the Godhead with three equilateral triangles. They added a fourth equilateral triangle, however, to embody the 22 laws of the Unified Field. Do you recall? I showed you how all 22 laws can be arrayed on seven consecutively wider levels that form an equilateral triangle. Finally, pre-Flood builders mounted all four equilateral triangles edge to edge atop a four-sided base representing the four-dimensional extent continuum to form—guess what?"

"A *pyramid*!" the archaeologist shouted.

"Yes!" Kaidan said with a smile. "Though the Egyptians, Mayans and others no longer knew what four triangles mounted on a square base represented, they hoped constructing the symbol itself might somehow restore some of the divine favor they knew had been forfeited.

"Another surviving representation of that long-ago forgotten Unified Field combines *two* oppositely pointed interlocked equilateral triangles, sometimes enclosed within a circle. The circle, when it is present, represents eternity. The down-pointing equilateral triangle represents God triune and the upward pointing equilateral triangle represents the 22-law Unified Field of Truth complete with every beautiful corollary rightfully in place. The interlocking of both triangles signifies the eternal interrelatedness of God and truth."

"Solomon's seal!" Rabbi Feinberg called from his chair.

"Otherwise known as ***The Star of David!***" Kaidan echoed. "How ironic, though, that David's star, which honors God as triune, should be favored to represent people who deny that God is triune even though one of their own names for him— *Elohim*—ends with '-im,' a plural suffix, and their own scripture quotes Elohim as saying, 'Let *us* create man in *our* image.'"

"Do other symbols trace back that far?" someone asked.

"Chinese lore also preserves a circle signifying eternity," Kaidan replied, "a circle containing two ovoid shapes instead of two interlocked triangles as in Judaism's Star of David. One ovoid shape is white, the other black. The white ovoid embraces a small black circle whereas the black ovoid has a small white circle embedded. Chinese philosophers call these two interactive ovoid shapes *'yin' and 'yang.'* Does anyone see which Harmony of truth pre-Flood designers had in mind when they created this design as a reminder ages ago?"

"The Harmony of Continua?" Justine called out moments later.

"That is correct! Now, please explain the connection," Kaidan requested.

"I thank you, kind Sir," Justine ventured tentatively, "for your vote of confidence that I can articulate an explanation that adequately captures the details of the symbol in terms of your teaching here. But I do not believe I am ready to do so. Thus I respectfully ask that you illuminate us all."

Justine waited, and then was grateful for Kaidan's reply: "In recognition of your honesty, and realizing that you are hearing much new information at this event, I will honor your request.

"The white ovoid represents God the Value Continuum. Conversely," Kaidan continued, "the black ovoid represents God's a-personal 'hyper-body'—the extent continuum. The small black circle within the white ovoid verifies that the extent continuum renders the Value Continuum forever omnipresent in the extent continuum. As for the small white circle within the black ovoid, it signifies that the Value Continuum reciprocally imparts meaning to the extent continuum by voluntarily creating extent density alterations and value loci within it."

Kaidan looked at Symposium attendees with an expression that seemed to invite everyone to weigh this different twist on a symbol familiar to all. After a quick scan of their notes on Kaidan's earlier teaching on the Harmony of Continua, Kent, James and Clyde all announced together, "Yes! A perfect match!"

Kaidan's face lit up with a smile as he said, "Whereas Chinese philosophers could only identify **yin and yang** rather strangely as 'male and female' principles that somehow undergird everything, now you know what pre-Flood originators of that pristine design had in mind. Remember that these symbols are far older than the religions that claim them now.

"A character designating God in ancient Chinese script strikingly represents God as a *triad* each part of which in turn has traits signified by the three sides of a triangle. In the pre-Flood era, each triangle represented one of the three-dimensional Persensions of the Value Continuum:

"Other symbols from ancient cultures correspond amazingly to the fifth of the seven Harmonies, where two categories of existence combine with two kinds of meaning. Note, for example, this recurring pattern from Inca art in South America:

"But there are still two more surviving pre-Flood symbols that are well known though by no means currently understood. Surely someone here can identify one or more of them." Kaidan paced back and forth on the dais, awaiting a reply.

People worldwide scanned their notes in vain. To help everyone, Kaidan clicked his remote, filling all seven screens with the Seven Harmonies of Truth, one Harmony per screen.

At last William Stansfield said, "Kaidan, I think I know what one of those other two surviving symbols might be. However, if I'm correct, that symbol's modern connotations are so opposite to its Unified Field significance that I hesitate even to name it, Sir."

"Bite the bullet, William. Name it," Kaidan urged.

Stansfield drew a deep breath and sighed. "The fifth Harmony's *four* laws present *two* measures of existence and *two* kinds of meaning that—combined in four different ways—define the primacy of God as sovereign over citizens, denizens and matter/energy in that order. What better form could we choose to depict four combinations of these same two sacred principles than simply to draw what in our time is known as a *swastika*, with its four two-part bent arms?"

Despite audible expressions of shock, Kaidan filled screen number 4 with a swastika. Each segment of its four bent arms bore words *defining* the four combinations of existence and meaning that belong to God, citizens, denizens and matter/energy respectively. The audience sighed with relief.

"We are privileged," Kaidan opined, "to undo the horror Nazism and neo-Nazism spread by misrepresenting this benign ancient symbol. It is a fitting though unfortunate example of a fallen citizen's ability to take something originally meant to glorify Valcon and make it a man-centered misrepresentation dishonoring Him. May the day come soon when a swastika will be widely regarded again with the awe it formerly inspired among Earth's earliest inhabitants, at least until the final years before the Flood."

The Symposium audience rose to applaud in agreement.

"Various other cultures celebrate what they call 'the sacred four' in other ways,'" Kaidan added, "symbolized, for example, by the four directions—east, west, north and south. Some North

American aboriginals celebrate the sacred four with four different colors or even with *horses* of four different colors."

An archaeologist who had posed a question earlier asked:

"Besides the pyramid, the Star of David, Chinese ovoids and the swastika, etc., I am thinking of another symbol that I believe may trace back to the ancient past."

"Speak your mind, Sir," Kaidan replied.

"The **bent scroll!**" the speaker replied. "Each segment of a bent scroll grows one unit longer as it corners around its center. So also each successive Harmony of the Unified Field features one more law than does its predecessor. Am I right?"

"Yes, you are!" Kaidan beamed as he displayed a bent scroll on all seven screens. "Believe me, these six symbols, though they persist unappreciated here on Earth, evoke awe throughout the 24-planet Federation. They remind us of the 22 laws of pre- and post-creation truth that are the basis of everything in the cosmos, including our relationship with Valcon.

"Now, I must reply to that other question as to why a Flood had to occur."

Chapter Eighteen
Factors that Delay Judgment

"God knows precisely where each of us stands in relation to him and to what is true," Kaidan resumed. "But God also weighs large-scale societal, even planet-wide ratios of goodness versus evil. What he measures evokes favor on one hand versus recompense on the other. Simply put, the cosmos is not a democracy. Prayer is always welcome, of course, but evil condoned remains unforgiven and unforgiven evil must always be subject to some degree of travail.

HOW VALCON REDUCES THE
AFFRONT EVIL BRANDISHES

"As I explained earlier, pending fulfillment of His special plan to vanquish evil convincingly in every possible way," Kaidan continued, "Valcon grants evil a delay of its final incarceration subject to the following six stipulations:

1) For the duration, evil may exist on just one planet.
2) Quasi-embodied instigators of evil must remain invisible.
3) Valcon abides anti-God humans as long as they are kept under 7th Harmony Deprivation. This in turn requires that they be enabled to infer the cosmos as naturalistic rather than proving God's existence. The more they construe science as justifying naturalism, the less guilty they are for ignoring God. Thus their judgment can not only be delayed but also be less severe when due. By the way, anti-God humans serve Valcon unwittingly if only by giving birth to or foster-parenting descendants, some of whom do turn in faith to Valcon!

4) Valcon employs the dual witness of creation and redemption, never irresistible force or coercion, to induce repentance and faith in all who render themselves persuadable.

5) Ironically, though they deserve better, redeemed folk must also endure a degree of 7th Harmony Deprivation for the duration. Sparing them exclusively from every trial would only add more insight to that which God-hating rebels are already guilty of rejecting. The greater the insight rebels get to spit on, the more intensely they taunt Valcon. The less they know, the less intense is that taunting. Redeemed people affected as a result will be well rewarded for their patience."

Philosopher Stansfield smiled to himself as he texted the Loop: *Now we know how extraterrestrials answer Job's famous question, why do the righteous have to suffer the same trials as those who are wicked?* Then, as William looked up to hear Kaidan relay the final stipulation in his series of six, he heard Kaidan say:

"As for the sixth and final stipulation, I will reveal it soon.

"So, then, as required by stipulations one and two, evil is indeed limited to this one planet *and* quasi-embodied fiends confined here do remain invisible to human eyes. But what of Valcon's third stipulation—the one that limits human insight?

"For some, God's invisibility is reason enough to deny that he exists. For terra-logicians, Valcon has so organized biological genera, for example, that anyone eager to deny that each species had to be created whole will be able to construe the record as pointing to a very gradual biological evolution instead. If you desire excuses no matter what, Valcon leaves 'excuses' on the lower shelf for you to find. But, of course, that is only 'for the duration,' as we say.

"English atheist Bertrand Russell was asked what he would say to God if, after death, he found his soul had survived the death of his body and that God does exist. Russell said he would ask, 'Sir, why did you not give me better evidence?'"

Kaidan said this looking straight at atheist Charles Stein, who, the previous evening, had said he planned to ask Kaidan to respond to Russell's objection that mankind was not obligated to believe in God unless God manifested himself to mankind in some physically visible way. Stein was getting his reply without asking.

"Russell's flippant response reveals an oversight," Kaidan argued. "Since God by definition is *infinite*, any visible form God might assume to prove his existence to Russell would have to be *finite* enough for Russell to comprehend. In that case, Russell—if so inclined—could dismiss God manifest in finite form as not infinite, hence not God. Requiring God to prove himself infinite by appearing in a finite form is puerile if not insulting. Anyone who rejects this cosmos as insufficient evidence for God is tragically dis-inviting himself from an eternal kingdom of love.

"Better to say, 'God, I get it! For you to be invisible is consistent with your infinity. I also get it that I can sense your benign Presence anywhere in the cosmos. I can even talk to you, not only with words I speak, but even in my thoughts as well.'

"Rebels usually have deeper reasons for disavowing God in any case. Aware that God and conscience require self-control, honesty, moral behavior and compassion, many choose disbelief so that conscience—denied its rightful Ally—can be violated with fewer qualms of inhibition. Others pride themselves as God-like enough without God. Both categories, unaware that they are under the influence of invisible tempters, destine themselves to share the fate of such.

HOW SPIRITUAL BLINDNESS FACILITATES DELAYED JUDGMENT

"As noted already, Valcon's third stipulation requires that God rejecters, if their judgment is to be delayed, must also be denied deeper levels of insight for the duration. For a case in point, Luke 23:34 records that Jesus, nailed to the cross, prayed:

"'Father, forgive them for they do not *know* what they are doing.' [emphasis added]

"The antithesis of that prayer would have been, 'These evildoers *know* that what they are doing constitutes a ghastly crime against none other than the Creator. *Punish them!*' Thus spiritual blindness actually shields incorrigible people from otherwise immediate wrath. That shielding, however, is only temporary. As scripture warns:

> "...people are destined to die once, and after that to face judgment. [Hebrews 9:27]

"As the Gospels record, Jesus warned crowds of people around him that teaching confirmed by divine miracles demands an appropriate response to God. Reaping insight about him without responding appropriately increases culpability. To listen and watch with zero intention to own up and repent is ill-advised.

"If Valcon finds one persuadable person amid five foreseen as incorrigible, he mediates saving truth to the one who is persuadable while hiding truth as best He can from those foreknown to respond in ways that will only add to their guilt. Better not to set people up for more than they already merit.

"Or, if Valcon foresees one persuadable person among five who are just barely so, he persuades the persuadable person first and then seeks to use him or her to appeal to the other five with the Gospel of Christ until they, too, are redeemed.

"In both instances, Valcon balances sovereignty with human free will on one hand and mercy with justice on the other. I declare to everyone listening worldwide that being a good listener to my teaching in this Symposium is not enough to seal your relationship with Valcon. You must stop treating Valcon as if he is of no consequence. *Invite Him now to birth a new value locus within you via the atoning sacrifice His Son made for you at such great cost to himself!*

"As for those quasi-embodied hence invisible anti-value loci who roam this crucible world, they possessed full knowledge of all Seven Harmonies of the Unified Field before they fell. That is what makes their guilt so great that redemption is not offered to them nor will it be offered to any other fully informed unfallen citizen who would ever follow their example despite everything Valcon has done and is willing to do.

"Also, it suits invisible evil beings perfectly if Valcon chooses to withhold knowledge of the Seven Harmonies from mankind forever. They are well aware that their final incarceration must be preceded by the re-introduction of Unified Field knowledge on this planet.

"By the way, *who* do you think persuaded you to define the cosmos as due to an explosion at a tiny point when omni-directional CBR was pointing all the while to a divinely circumscribed Sphere of Origin? *They* did! Thinking yourselves wise, you were channeling their illogical hatred for Valcon.

"Now! Let me explain the immediate problem that overshadows Earth even as I speak. Despite the earlier six stipulations Valcon instituted to withhold judgment from this planet, evil has increased so *horribly* here that mere 7th Harmony Deprivation can no longer delay planet-wide accelerated judgment. Just as terra-economists measure the rise and fall of a nation's Gross Domestic Product (GDP), terra-society is plunging dangerously close to its *Gross Enormity Limit*, i.e., the point at which 7th Harmony Deprivation must step aside and give place to levels of judgment that are much more immediate and severe.

"Hear me explain where planet Earth stands with Valcon at this very moment."

Chapter Nineteen
A Crucible Planet's
Pending Flashpoint

Kaidan resumed, "So let's ask: what degree of societal evil offends *omniscient* Valcon so grievously that 7th Harmony Deprivation's moderate retribution no longer assuages his wrath?

"On Earth, if homicide, rape and robbery statistics are just a little lower than previously, that serves as an acceptable *status quo*. Abortion, adultery, divorce, drug-dealing, pornography pandering, addiction, child or parental abuse and abandonment statistics rarely make the news. When Valcon measures evil, however, he holds not just evil deeds and words but even 'the thoughts and intents of the heart' to account.

"To explain when Valcon decides that a given society, such as your pre-Flood civilization, has reached its Enormity Limit," Kaidan commented, "let me quote words the Apostle John penned two millennia ago. Describing *four* categories of people who—being 'of age' hence mentally responsible—are deemed suited for 7th Harmony Deprivation's moderate retribution, John wrote:

"Let him who does wrong continue to do wrong;
let the vile person continue to be vile;
let the one who does right continue to do right; and
let the holy person continue to be holy. [Revelation 22:11]

"So it is that a certain percentage of unredeemed people 'do wrong' without sinking to levels of utter 'vileness' and cruelty. Similarly, a percentage of redeemed people 'do well' while falling short of outstandingly holy endeavor in Valcon's service. Valcon sees the vile as **Category I _Rebels_**. He assesses people in the next rank as **Category II** *Wrong-doers*. Referring as he does only to 'of age' citizens, John's list omits young children, including the pre-born. These are Valcon's **Category III** *Innocents*.

"Most redeemed people comprise Valcon's **Category IV** *Well-doers*, people who devote at least part of their lives to serving God, their own families, and perhaps even neighbors and strangers as well. A few scattered here and there throughout the world may even resemble the biblical character *Job*—people who, despite an absence of Scripture, glean enough insight about God from creation and conscience alone to supplicate the Creator for mercy and become men of peace. In Psalm 50:5 God refers to such as 'this consecrated people who made a covenant with me by sacrifice.' Jesus also referred to such in John 10:16, declaring,

> "'I have other sheep that are not of *this* sheep pen. I must bring them also. They too will listen to my voice, and there shall be *one* flock and *one* shepherd.' [emphasis added]

"Devout high-achievers are Valcon's **Category V** *Proclaimers*. More about such later.

"As long as the *sum* of Category III **Innocents** plus Category IV **Well-doers** plus Category V **Proclaimers** exceeds the sum of **Wrong-doers** and evil **Rebels** on the first and second levels of Valcon's ethics 'graph,' 7th Harmony Deprivation keeps on preempting destructive retribution until 'the duration' ends.

MORE ABOUT CATEGORY II WRONG-DOERS

"Typical 'Category II' wrong-doers may snitch items they think will not be missed but they do not rob at gunpoint nor do they break in to plunder. Legitimate self-interest may motivate them to be model employers, good employees, clever businesspersons and creative thinkers who rarely sacrifice resources or time to help the needy. Some get addicted to tobacco and/or alcohol but mostly they avoid drug addiction and/or drug trafficking. Many get angry but they do not kill except when abortion is preferred to an unwanted pregnancy. They may fantasize about immorality but they do not rape, commit adultery or view pornography.

"Category II folk may fail to discipline themselves or their children but they agree that convicted pirates, fraudsters, rapists and murderers be incarcerated or executed. They may disrespect a spouse and mistreat a child—*but never to the extent of abandoning either!* They say they believe in God but live as if there is no God. Category II folk befriend those who, like themselves, are also lackadaisical about God. They may even smirk at anyone who expresses love for God overtly.

"Let no Category II Wrong-doer assume that merely avoiding Category I vileness makes him acceptable to Valcon apart from Christ. Category II persons are just as responsible as heinous rebels to approach Valcon humbly by repenting and asking to be forgiven and cleansed via the Atonement that Christ has made available for mankind. That said, to the degree that Category II people outnumber Category I rebels significantly, the Enormity Limit of both categories combined is reduced.

"So also, to the degree that Valcon's Category III Innocents, his Category IV Well-doers and his Category V Proclaimers out-percentage both lower Categories, Earth's Enormity Limit is even more greatly reduced. Now perhaps you can better grasp why Jesus spoke of righteous people as 'the *salt* of the Earth,' salt being a major preservative.

"If, on the other hand, the sum of Category I Rebels plus Category II Wrong-doers exceeds the sum of righteous people in Categories III, IV and V, judgment stalks its prey as it stalked and then destroyed Earth's pre-Flood civilization ages ago.

THE FATE OF THE PRE-FLOOD CIVILIZATION

"Genesis 6:5-12 informs us that:

"The LORD saw how great the wickedness of the human race had become on the earth, and that every inclination of the thoughts of the human heart was only evil all the time... Now the earth was corrupt in God's sight and full of violence. God saw how corrupt the earth had become, for all the people on earth had corrupted their ways.

"Tragically, if vicious rebels and grossly apathetic wrong-doers not only outnumber the righteous but also begin killing or oppressing the righteous and each other, an even more rapid plunge toward oblivion ensues. People in that situation begin birthing fewer Category III Innocents. In Earth's pre-Flood civilization—copied centuries later by Sodom and Gomorrah—procreation-less same-sex liaisons further undermined 7th Harmony Deprivation's viability by reducing the number of Category III Innocents being added to the human scene.

"Valcon's primary command to mankind was, and still is, 'Be fruitful! Increase in numbers! Fill the earth!' Ignoring Valcon's prime directive, pre-Flood mankind blindly revectored itself straight back toward *auto-extinction*. Rather than idly watch mankind dwindle gradually in violation of his prime command, Valcon simply accelerated the already-opted extinction process via the Flood and then restarted mankind with a righteous few in a significantly resurfaced world. There was, however, one more reason for the Flood that I have yet to mention.

STILL ANOTHER FLOOD PRECIPITANT

"If you recall, earlier in my presentation I mentioned six stipulations that facilitate fallen mankind's subjection to that milder form of divine judgment known as 7th Harmony Deprivation. At that time I presented five of those stipulations but promised to describe the sixth and final stipulation later.

"*Now* is the right time to reveal Valcon's sixth stipulation for delaying judgment via 7th Harmony Deprivation. Here it is:

6) Embodied perpetrators of evil must be denied knowledge of the Unified Field of Truth.

"People of Earth, hear me! The sixth stipulation warns that for mankind to be subject to mere 7th Harmony Deprivation, knowledge of all seven Harmonies of the Unified Field must be hidden from mankind for the duration. Remaining evil despite comprehending cosmically special knowledge renders rebels far guiltier in Valcon's sight than otherwise. Impenitent sinners must either be denied that ultimate level of knowledge or else be subject to more severe retribution.

"As of now, you are all well aware of what has happened on Earth this very day. Valcon sent me here to remove the final stipulation which—from the time of the Flood until now—has secured 7th Harmony Deprivation as Valcon's way of responding to evil on this planet. As of now everything has changed. Every government and every lawmaker must understand that the ultimate King is imposing his rule and his laws in place of theirs. Every person who is not already a citizen subordinate to Valcon's rule must seek citizenship in the ultimate Kingdom before its gates close or else you will experience the ultimate 'deportation.'

"To help you understand, let me teach you a little history.

WHAT NAÏVE ARKONANS ONCE URGED VALCON TO DO

"Long before I was born on Arkona, Valcon announced that Earth was to be his 'crucible' planet. He set Earth aside as the site for a plan that will enable him to forestall recurrences of evil forever while keeping free will still free. He also announced that Adam and Eve and their descendants—consistent with 7th Harmony Deprivation—would be limited to a lifespan not more than 120 years and also that knowledge of the Unified Field must be entirely hidden from them for as long as it might take for God's plan to culminate.

"As a race of immortal beings blessed with Unified Field knowledge, we Arkonans could not imagine how awful it would be not to comprehend such truth and to feel death closing in that quickly. Moved with pity, we persuaded ourselves that comprehending the Unified Field would persuade stubborn Earthlings to obey Valcon, especially if they were given more time to weigh the options.

"We pleaded with Valcon so urgently that finally—so that **we** might learn a major lesson about evil—he gave us permission to impart Unified Field knowledge to Adam's descendants. He also agreed to adjust 7th Harmony Deprivation by extending man's lifespan to cover multiple centuries.

"The bonding we anticipated among Earthlings did indeed prevail for a time. Adam's descendants gratefully learned all 22 laws of the Unified Field from us and even used the seven symbols of that Field as reminders. A majority of Adam's descendants honored Valcon and lived as Category IV and V devotees.

"Eventually, some citizens from Arkona even married daughters of Eve and fathered children, offspring who of course also grew up to be unfallen immortals inasmuch as an inverted value locus can be transmitted only by a fallen *male*.

"Unfallen arko-human immortals, born immune to 7th Harmony Deprivation, began applying their full 7th Harmony powers the way modern man exploits heavy machinery. Unleashing their powers to that extent enabled them to help early mankind construct amazing edifices and monoliths. These exploits, as Genesis 6:4 records, earned arko-humans honor as 'heroes of old, men of renown.'

"Gradually, however, sons of Adam—constantly denied those same powers and steadily aging—became filled with resentment against Valcon and us!

"Just as Valcon foreknew would happen, a grievous change emerged. Horrified, we saw evil roiling on all sides until finally Valcon's retribution came down in the form of a mega-disaster made awesomely more severe because, by sinning against the Unified Field knowledge we gave them, the wicked were no longer merely evil. By insisting that they be given Unified Field knowledge, we had made it possible for humans to render themselves *hyper*-evil!

"Rebellion was inevitable in any case, but we rued our part in making it more severe via our misguided compassion. No one knows better than Valcon how to deal with evil.

"Then, following the Flood, everything changed. No more long lifespans for mankind. No more extra-terrestrials marrying Earth women or even interacting overtly with humans. And especially, no more Unified Field knowledge for mankind, at least not until the end is near. As for me, I was not involved in that part of Earth history. In terms of Earth time, I am only 4,537 years old. The Flood happened prior to my birth.

HOW THE BIBLE ITSELF HINTS AT 'CLASSIFIED' TRUTH

"And now, on the subject of God mercifully hiding classified knowledge from mankind lest 7th Harmony Deprivation be interrupted, again I invite Dr. Kent Madison to cite for us biblical texts hinting at that same divine prohibition."

Kent was amazed. Pondering Kaidan's teaching, he had just then begun recalling biblical hints that deeper truth remains, as it were, 'classified' relative to mankind. Was Kaidan reading his mind? Rising to full height, Kent began to recite from memory:

"Amazing Teacher, as best I recall, Paul the Apostle wrote these words in his second letter to Jesus' followers at Corinth:

"I know a man in Christ who fourteen years ago was caught up to the third heaven...and heard inexpressible things, *things that no one is permitted to tell*...because of these surpassingly great revelations...in order to keep me from becoming conceited, I was given a thorn in my flesh.... [II Corinthians 12:2-7, emphasis added]

"Kaidan, I also offer another text in which Paul posits God as hiding truth that is 'unsafe' for mankind, while using 'safe' truth to fulfill merciful goals without divulging classified secrets in the process. Here is a paraphrase of 1 Corinthians 1:21:

"For since *in the wisdom of God* the world through its wisdom did not know him, God was pleased through the foolishness of what was preached to save those who believe.

"God's decision to 'work undercover' so as to hide classified truth from defiant men had been acknowledged many centuries earlier, as revealed in this paraphrase of Psalm 8:2:

"From the lips of children and infants you have ordained praise because of your enemies, to silence the foe and the avenger. [A paraphrase]

"Apparently, Valcon, by keeping his enemies in the dark as to what is really going on, prevents them from reacting in ways that would arouse Recompense. Indeed, if episodes of judgment against an overtly defiant few become too frequent, surely such will be seen as obscuring Valcon's overtures of mercy to mankind at large. Valcon deems it better to dispense mercy first and reserve the task of final judgment until later. Another related text that just came to mind, Kaidan, is Deuteronomy 29:29:

"The secret things belong to the LORD our God, but the things revealed belong to us and to our children forever…

"I'm sure there are other Scriptures that also reinforce this same theme."

"Thank you, Dr. Madison," Kaidan replied, "but there is still one more text I must add to your excellent list, a text for which I feel a special affinity. It is Revelation chapter 10. Dr. Engle, since you earlier asked Dr. Madison about obtaining your own electronic copy of the Bible, I feel certain he will be happy to lend you his copy for a few moments. Please, on his behalf, read Revelation chapter 10 aloud for us."

KAIDAN'S SPECIAL EMPATHY FOR REVELATION CHAPTER 10

In his entire life, James had not read even one verse of scripture in private, let alone read an entire passage aloud before a worldwide audience. He was about to ask Kent to check his own device to find Revelation chapter 10 for him. Instead, James found that Kent had anticipated the need. As if foreknowing Kaidan's request, Kent handed his own tablet over to James. The words of Revelation 10 already appeared on the display. James, in awe, enunciated these solemn words:

"Then I saw another mighty angel coming down from heaven. He was robed in a cloud, with a rainbow above his head; his face was like the sun and his legs were like fiery pillars. He was holding a little scroll, which lay open in his hand. He planted his right foot on the sea and his left foot on the land, and he gave a loud shout like the roar of a lion. When he shouted, the voices of the seven thunders spoke. And when the seven thunders spoke, I was about to write; but I heard a voice from heaven say, 'Seal up what the seven thunders have said and do not write it down....'"

Gasps from the entire forum audience interrupted James.

"James, look at the screens!" Kent gasped.

James looked up to see what had transfixed the entire forum. John's vision of an angel swathed in cloud, crowned with a rainbow and descending with a scroll lying open in one hand, now filled the left two-thirds of each screen. Likewise the very words James had been reading from Revelation chapter 10 were also there—translated as needed—in silver characters to the right of that august figure on every screen.

At first, the glow shimmering on the angel's face disguised his features. But, by the time James looked up from the tablet, the light had faded enough for James and everyone watching worldwide to recognize that angel as *none other than Kaidan himself*! Kent, recalling how often Kaidan's smile had seemed to glow with actual light, now recognized that light, not only as *real*, but also as able to vary its intensity.

"That was you!" Homer Grassley gasped. "You were here 2,000 years ago!"

"Yes!" Kaidan responded. "This is not my first mission to Earth. I came here two millennia ago with fellow messengers from Arkona. We all had to learn Greek for that prior visit, just as I have had to master English for this occasion. *Who else* do you suppose introduced John to '24 elders'? *Who else* told him that although God is three Persons who are One, it is also acceptable to speak of the '*seven* spirits of God'—known to us today as the seven dimensions: intellect, emotion and will accompanied by length, breadth, height and time? That is why John, thus informed, became the first human since pre-Flood days to refer to 'the *seven* spirits of God,' as John did in Revelation 1:4, 3:1 and again in 4:5.

"Yes, two millennia ago I appeared to the Apostle John as you see on screen. When seven colleagues of mine quoted the seven motifs written on the scroll that lay open in my hand, their voices echoed like thunder in an oncoming storm. Appropriately, John referred to those seven motifs as 'the seven thunders.'

"Dare I ask, can anyone within the sound of my voice surmise what *were* those seven motifs John heard and then identified as 'the seven thunders'?"

William Stansfield stood tall and called aloud, "The Seven Harmonies of that beautiful Unified Field of Truth that you have explained to us in this Symposium!"

"Precisely!" Kaidan exclaimed. "For my next question, can anyone here decode why I placed my right foot in the sea and kept my left foot on *land*?"

After seven or eight seconds of focused thought, Justine Hobbs bravely replied, "Noble friend of our crucible planet, I believe **'sea'** in your imagery represents the *pre*-creation part of the 22 laws your associates were about to articulate. **'Land'** represents Valcon's *post*-creation addition to that series. By connecting sea and land with one grand stance, you denoted the perfect interrelatedness of pre-creation and post-creation truth."

"Another precisely correct response!" Kaidan beamed.

Justine got a standing ovation.

"What then of the cloud and the rainbow?" Kaidan asked.

None other than geologist Rolf Jorgensen, still abashed from the earlier quizzing but also still intrigued, asked, "Could the **cloud** represent the comet-induced Flood which, by punishing mankind and erasing knowledge of the Unified Field from our entire planet, lowered mankind's culpability such that 7th Harmony deprivation could replace wrath at least until now? Is it possible that the **rainbow**, reminiscent of the one that appeared right after the Flood, could likewise represent *the new order of things* that has prevailed from the Great Flood until now under 7th Harmony Deprivation's mercifully moderated levels of retribution?"

"Well surmised! Thank you, Dr. Jorgensen," Kaidan said, only then to ask, "Why then did a voice command John *not* to write what he heard the seven thunders say? Why was he ordered instead to *seal up* that obviously classified knowledge?"

Clyde Smith replied, "I assume transcribing what the seven thunders said would have restored previously expunged 'top secret' Unified Field insight to mankind. Knowing mankind at large was still in no way ready to honor such special knowledge appropriately, Valcon wanted John alone to hear it but not to write it down. He knew a majority of mankind would tragically repeat the pre-Flood race's culpable failure to appreciate what had been revealed, thereby triggering still another cataclysmic retribution at a premature moment. Am I correct?"

"Yes!" Kaidan responded. "And as you might guess, John heard the seven thunders say the same words Paul had heard on a different occasion and was forbidden to repeat on this planet. But this crucial passage has still another symbolism I ask you to decode. Note that I, in verse 9, gave that same open scroll to John and asked him to *eat it*. I forewarned John that although the scroll would taste as sweet as honey in his mouth, it would turn *bitter* in his stomach. And so it happened. What did *that* represent?"

Homer stood to respond: "I suspect 'sweetness' denotes the initial pleasure of *understanding* the Unified Field as the basis of all that is true. 'Bitterness in the stomach,' conversely, represents the aftermath of that privilege: *the obligation to conduct one's thoughts, desires and actions in ways that are consistent with such consummate knowledge, despite being indwelt by a fallen nature all the while, as even the Apostle John was while still alive!"*

"Precisely," Kaidan said. "Thus I urge all of you to do what others here have already done—trust Valcon to birth a new value locus within you. Please stand with Homer if that is your choice."

Dozens more responders rose up decisively.

WILL MANKIND TURN 'HYPER-EVIL' AGAIN?

"But—Kaidan!" Kent queried, "Via this vast worldwide network, you have enlightened millions of us afresh with the same insight which ages ago became a catalyst *for* the Flood, only then to be expunged *by* the Flood. Does Valcon foreknow that mankind at last is ready to respond to such knowledge *wisely*? Or have you on purpose enlightened impenitent mankind afresh with classified wisdom so as to render mankind once again *hyper-evil*, thus triggering a final apocalypse because God has decided that Earth's time is up?"

"Indeed, Dr. Madison," Kaidan replied soberly; "Valcon at last has harvested from Earth's total population *almost* the total host of God and truth welcomers he requires to bear witness to his grace across the vastness of the cosmos. Following their pre-glory mission here on Earth, *they* will be privileged to fulfill an on-going mission in ages to come by testifying *for* Valcon and *against* evil on every planet that is yet to be peopled with unfallen freewill beings in billions of galaxies. Because of their awesomely unique testimony, evil will never recur.

"Throughout this encounter, most of you have honored me as at least technologically superior to you if not also superior in other ways as well. Yet I want you to know that in another sense, *I* recognize myself as *inferior* to every Earth-person who, despite being tethered to a fallen value locus, has received salvation via the atonement provided by Jesus, the Persension of Omni-sentience incarnate.

"I say that because as one who has neither experienced evil nor been rescued from it, I am totally incapable of testifying against evil in the profound ways that you are destined to fulfill! Your testimony alone can keep the cosmos immune to recurrences of evil on billions of yet-to-be-peopled worlds. When it comes to that immense privilege, Arkonans like me can only stand by and watch as spectators, not participants.

"All of you listening to my voice are invited to claim that superior privilege as your destiny provided you do so before the door of opportunity slams shut, as did the door of that long-ago ark. Now let me explain why, earlier, I said '*almost* the total host.'

"Actually, what Valcon is close to completing is much more than merely a 'harvest.' Just as every harvest, according to Jewish law, had to be *preceded* by a relatively small ingathering called the '*first-fruits*,' and *followed* by a final, relatively small ingathering called 'the *gleaning*,' so also Jeremiah foresaw a pre-harvest ingathering when he wrote the following:

"**Israel** was holy to the LORD, the *firstfruits* of his harvest. [Jeremiah 2:3, emphasis added]

"So also the Apostle Paul referred to that same **harvest** as a sizeable ingathering followed later by what—also according to Jewish law—could only be called a *gleaning* phase.

FIRSTFRUITS PRECEDE; GLEANING FOLLOWS

"Paul the Apostle wrote:

"Israel has experienced a *hardening* in part *until* <u>the full number of the Gentiles</u> has come in. And in this way *all Israel will be saved.* [Romans 11:25-26, emphasis added]

"Paul's reference to 'the full number of the Gentiles' coming in refers primarily to those described later in the Apocalypse as 'some from every, nation, tribe, people and language' [Revelation 7:9]. These comprise the harvest ingathered by the ultimately worldwide witness of the true Church from the Day of Pentecost until now. That number includes also Job-like 'people of peace' credited in John 3:21, Psalm 50:5 and Matthew 25 as redeemed by Jesus *incognito*—both before and after the Day of Pentecost—in response to their having sought mercy from 'the God of heaven' at threshold moments.

"That number also includes the majority of mankind that has died or been killed via miscarriage, abortion, still-birth or death in childhood. This innocent two-thirds of mankind, having died without willfully violating a single 7th Harmony Ideal, is covered automatically by Christ's atonement. Jesus, in the Gospels, refers to children as those to whom 'the kingdom of heaven belongs.' The Apostle Paul also affirms childhood innocence in Romans 7 verses 9 and 11.

"Obviously this huge number includes the *children* of people who so lived and died as to isolate themselves forever from Valcon, hence also from their own children who died while still innocent.

"Yet when Paul avers that 'all Israel will be saved' subsequent to the earlier-described harvest of Gentiles, an after-harvest gleaning phase is implied. Paul foresaw a future very significant change of heart by a significant minority, perhaps even a majority, of currently Jesus-disdaining *Jewish* people *following* the aforementioned worldwide ingathering of 'the full number of the *Gentiles.*' In that final phase, 144,000 Jews will startle the world by proclaiming the Gospel of Jesus Christ as the true Messiah and Savior of mankind. Add the late responders they will lead to faith to the other categories mentioned above and approximately 77 percent of mankind will have been saved.

"God's victory over evil incarcerated in this crucible world can in no way be described as pyrrhic!"

Then, looking directly at James, Kaidan said, "By way of an extended reply to Dr. Madison, please read further from that same chapter in the Apocalypse." James read:

"Then the angel I had seen standing on the sea and on the land raised his right hand to heaven. And he swore by him who lives forever and ever, who created the heavens and all that is in them, the earth and all that is in it, and the sea and all that is in it, and said, *'There will be no more delay!* But in the days when the seventh angel is about to sound his trumpet, *the mystery of God* will be accomplished, just as he announced to his servants the prophets.'

"Soon the 24 elders, along with hosts of citizens from the 24-planet Federation, will exult before God over those he has redeemed, declaring that now at last the 'manifold wisdom of God' has been so revealed as to assure that no rebellion will ever occur again anywhere in the entire cosmos! Glory and honor and might be to our God forever and ever!"

Chapter Twenty
Fallen Mankind's Grievous History

"People of Earth, mankind this very day is crossing a new threshold," Kaidan said solemnly. "Via this historic gathering I have explained a major part of 'the mystery of God' by defining God, Creator of everything, as the infinite Value Continuum in whom are found the three immutable Persensions. I have also unveiled the 22 laws that are nothing less than the Seven Harmonies of Interstellar Truth. I have also explained why Valcon permitted evil initially and how he is subsequently achieving a moral victory over evil that is so resplendently convincing that no matter how many more freewill beings Valcon creates in all of space and time, none will ever abuse free will again forever!

"I have also singularly validated the witness of Christians who proclaim Jesus as providing redemption for everyone who wants to be reconciled to God and delivered from evil. I even revealed how Jesus ingeniously atoned for the sin of mankind by subjecting himself to undeserved 7th Harmony Deprivation, thus enabling him to juxtapose the debt the 7th Harmony owes to him so as to cancel the debt that every of-age repentant human owes for having violated Harmony Seven's six immortal Ideals.

"Your leaders everywhere invited me to educate you with precepts from the science of another world. Have I not done exactly that by pyramiding truth upon truth before you? Yes! Thus I have rendered every of-age listener responsible to submit, not to me nor to Arkona but to Valcon, who created you.

"Anyone who refuses to submit to Valcon now can no longer count on being subject to mere 7th Harmony Deprivation. There can be no more 'delay,' hence severer judgment impends!

"If you wonder why Valcon sent me here to alter your standing before him so unexpectedly, it is due to a catastrophic rise in the enormity of evil that has been ballooning on Earth since the close of the 19ᵗʰ century. Thus I must now parlay a list of specific issues that mankind must correct if it is to avoid another apocalyptic destruction. Previously I invited your interaction with me on various topics. Now, for these next twenty minutes or so, please allow me to monologue as follows.

CONTRASTING EARTH'S PRESENT-DAY ENORMITY WITH EARLIER TIMES

"Following the Roman Empire's 'same-race' enslavement of Slavs (hence the word 'slave') and Serbs (hence the word 'serve'), Muslims initiated 'other-race' enslavements of sub-Saharan Africans. Some Muslim slavers brought shiploads of African slaves from Zanzibar off the coast of Kenya to be sold in Arabia and Egypt. Others force-marched hundreds of thousands of captives north across 1400 miles of Sahara sand to be sold in Moroccan, Algerian, Tunisian and Libyan bazaars.

"Over time, European nations noted the advantage of purchasing other-race slaves from Muslims in North Africa. Runaway slaves of a different race were more readily identified and captured. Then European nations themselves began sailing around West Africa to purchase captives directly from 'the Slave Coast.' Africans, by the way, deemed Muslim slavers more heinous than their European counterparts in that Muslim slavers commonly emasculated captive African men.

"Great Britain, already a slave-trading villain in the late 1700s, proceeded to make itself even more equivalent to a modern Colombia drug cartel by deliberately addicting Chinese merchants to opium so as to be able to extort valuable silk from them in exchange for the drug. Their vileness incited the Opium War. Then at last the new flowering of a former benign influence began persuading much of Europe to mend its ways.

"In northern Europe, Waldensian, Cathar, Moravian, Puritan, Pietistic, Wesleyan and Anabaptist *proclaimers*—spurning the opposition of pompously self-absorbed hierarchical Christianity—began recovering apostolic zeal by spreading the good news of salvation via prevenient grace both at home and even far beyond the shores of Europe and North America. What these friends of God and mankind lacked by way of cathedral-building skill, they made up for with *evangelistic prowess!*

"In the spirit of that same benign charisma, John Newton, William Wilberforce and others at last persuaded an apathetic parliament in London to abolish Britain's slave trade empire-wide. Britain began seizing other nations' slave ships and returning captives back to their homelands. Abraham Lincoln eventually presided over a war that abolished slavery in America's South.

"Meanwhile, back in Europe and North America, John and Charles Wesley, George Whitefield, Jonathan Edwards, American circuit riders, Charles Finney, Dwight L. Moody, R. A. Torrey and later Billy Sunday and Billy Graham in the 1900s led millions to faith on both sides of the Atlantic. Proclaimers such as these laid the moral foundation for the ethical fortitude and public trust that lifted Western nations to higher levels of accomplishment and idealism than had ever been achieved large-scale in human history.

"William Carey, Adoniram Judson, George and Sarah Boardman, Robert Morrison, David Livingstone, Hudson and Maria Taylor, Lars Skrefsrud, Amy Carmichael, Jonathan and Rosalind Goforth, Mary Slessor, Gladys Aylward, Lottie Moon, Bill Bright, Loren Cunningham and thousands like them blazed trails for the message of Christ in India, Burma, China, Korea, Africa and other far-flung areas. Colleges, schools, hospitals and clinics proliferated where none had ever existed. John Sung's ministry so revived Chinese Christians that rather than flounder under Communist oppression, they *flourished!*

"The words of the Prophet Daniel aptly anticipated the blessing dispensed by heroes such as the above:

"Those who are wise will shine like the brightness of the heavens, and those who lead many to righteousness, like the stars for ever and ever. [Daniel 12:3]

"Inspired mainly by the shining example of these many Category V Proclaimers, Category IV Well-doers also engaged in many more godly endeavors. Repentance by Wrong-doers and even some Evil-doers began to reduce mankind's rates of divorce, adultery, incest, murder, rape, prostitution, pedophilia, abortion, addictions, theft, kidnapping, extortion, blasphemy and abuse.

"Not only so, but incorrigible criminals assuredly convicted of brutal capital crimes were duly executed rather than being pampered with food, lodging, education, free medical and dental care and other privileges at the expense of those they victimize—i.e., taxpayers generically.

"The USA, Canada, Australia and New Zealand came to the aid of dozens of European and Asian nations precipitously shattered by German and Japanese nihilism and greed. Triumphant at last over the nihilists, the Allies promptly showed mercy to war-abetting German and Japanese populations by restoring their economies and granting them the very freedoms they themselves would have denied to the majority of mankind. *That* was the finest hour in the political and societal history of this entire planet!

"Everyone across our 24-planet Federation exulted as percentages of Proclaimers, Well-doers and not-yet-of-age Innocents at last exceeded the number of Wrong-doers and Rebels over much of Earth! The need for Valcon to impose forceful judgment subsided correspondingly. Yet invisible demon hosts still had violent Communist atheism and equally violent pseudo-theistic Islamic nihilism on hand for future genocidal purposes. Humanism would also prove to be a stealthy foe.

"Throughout the 19th and at least the first half of the 20th century, parents plus teachers and professors at various levels of education taught moral responsibility if not actual belief in God. But thereafter, enormously offensive changes in education policy became dominant and godly parental influence diminished. Even where it still exists, many godless educators revel to undermine it.

"And now, at last, evil's tenure on Earth is about to culminate only to be replaced by Valcon's totally righteous reign.

THE FINAL METASTASIS AND DOWNFALL OF EVIL

"Following Earth's relatively idyllic 19th century came a 20th century marred with brutal Nazism, Japanese expansionism and violent Communist atheism oppressing hundreds of millions of people with ultra-destructive modern weaponry. The latter horror still opposes the Chinese population's widespread belief in Shang-Di—Valcon's 'a.k.a.' in the Mandarin language. It also forbids the semi-theistic but astutely moral precepts of Confucius to be taught to millions across much of Southeast Asia. Over time, Stalin and Mao and their henchmen brainwashed millions of Chinese children such that they betrayed their own parents to death. Later these horrors segued to the slaughter of millions more via outbreaks of genocide in Burundi, Bosnia, Cambodia, Viet Nam and Laos.

"In the early 1800s, hard-core Evil-doers accounted for a mere 5 percent of mankind. Now tens of millions more of that ilk roam unpunished or relax at ease in prisons following crimes of murder, rape, fraud, pedophilia, break-ins, pimping, prostitution, pornography, fornication, adultery, perversion, drug dealing, drug addiction, alcoholism, occultism, kidnapping, human trafficking, flash-mobbing and internet robbery.

"Terra-police blotters list only a tiny part of what Valcon sees and forbids. Abortion, since Roe versus Wade, cascades worldwide. Mankind now kills many millions of its own babies every year, with the average number of abortions steadily rising year by year in many nations. That cascade will keep increasing until and unless severe judgment intervenes.

"Male and female homosexuality proliferates even more with the legalization of same-sex 'marriage.' Little do judges and lawmakers realize how direly they offend Valcon and endanger mankind by legalizing abortion and same-sex marriage.

"Both rulings, because of the cascading effects they induce, are incipiently genocidal. In Valcon's eyes, all who inscribe such laws and the governments that enforce them are equivalent to criminals spreading a virus deadly enough to assure extinction. Valcon's policy in the past has been not to wait for already-in-effect genocide to worsen, but to interrupt it with severe judgment and begin again with a more faithful human remnant. I am here to warn mankind that he is about to unfold that policy again. This time, however, it will come with a new twist.

"Millions among you refuse to emulate the choices honorably married husbands and wives made to birth children, raise and educate them to live productive lives. Such gross presumption by the young adds to the tonnage of human guilt. It grieves Valcon when the next generation refuses to 'pay forward' that same favor by at least hoping to marry and bear children.

"Add blasphemers, dishonest vote-counters, biased judges, media stars and moguls who abet social ills. Add also hundreds of millions of teenagers who, responding to continuous media enticement, mar their psychological fitness to form stable marriages by indulging in sexual promiscuity, drug use and alcoholism early in life. These problems alone assure that the next generation's divorce, adultery, abortion and crime levels will soar exponentially above what currently prevails.

"Recently, for example, a school teacher in Canada, standing in front of an assembly of eighth-grade children (ages 12 and 13), encouraged them to begin experimenting with both same-sex and heterosexual relationships just to see which they like best. Potentially, same-sex liaisons—which require no condoms and entail no expense for abortion—will be the favored option. Auto-extinction lurks in the shadows, leaving mankind with that many fewer infants and babies to offset Valcon's view of terra-society as brazenly inviting destruction.

"Valcon's prime directive is still in force and with good reason. Every doctor, nurse, teacher, bus driver, plumber, carpenter, electrician, mechanic, farmer, pilot, politician, soldier, police officer, first responder and other service person has to begin as a baby. All such must be birthed and raised or the number of people in such professions diminishes, much to mankind's increasing detriment. In the pre-Flood era, people actually killed each other competing for service providers. Only external judgment can mercifully interrupt and extinguish such chaos.

THE SPECIAL CASE OF ISLAM

"Ironically, Earth's Muslim population, despite sourcing frequent brutal violence, forbids aborting babies. This is partly because Muslim strategists encourage high Muslim birthrates so as to enable Islam eventually to surpass the total number of the rest of mankind. Maintaining high birth rates signifies a Muslim plot to over-flood other societies where birth rates as low as 1.3 babies per woman are foolishly fostered. Abetting that same stratagem, Islam forbids homosexuality on the part of Muslim males while encouraging non-Muslims to accept it. A recent American President endorsed same-sex marriage in America and even urged African nations to accept homosexuality as normal.

"Some Muslims in Asia are so eager to exploit Muslim children as suicide bombers that other Muslims now prefer to enroll their children in Christian schools, hoping thus to isolate their children from any such monstrous influence that might exist in exclusively Muslim schools. Their parental heart cry is akin to 'We want our children to *grow* up, not *blow* up!'

"At this point let me pause to pay Adolf Hitler one 'compliment' of sorts. Hitler stopped short of claiming divine inspiration for a book he wrote called *Mein Kampf*. Had he added that claim, reading *Mein Kampf* would have rendered Nazi thugs even more implacably disposed to wage war.

"Let me also pay that same quasi-'compliment' to Karl Marx and Friedrich Engels. Conceivably, had they claimed divine inspiration for their book called *Das Kapital*, Communists might have begun strapping on suicide vests in pursuit of divine reward for atrocities perpetrated as a service for God.

"Mohammed, however, *did* claim divine inspiration for warmongering in two 7th century treatises: the Koran and the Hadith. Over 100 Koranic verses urge Muslims to attack non-Muslims in response to fatwas. Muslims are urged to subject kafirs who yield—called *dhimmis*—to endless social abasement under Muslim rule. In five Koran verses Mohammed titillates jihadists by promising them endless sexual pleasure as a heavenly reward.

"Fully Koranic Islam thus abets *the ultimate metastasis of evil*. Converts are persuaded that God, far from *forbidding* murder, *rewards* murderers by catering eternally to their sexual lust. Male ISIS and Boko Haram zealots are thus motivated as much by their own gonads as by supposedly sacred verses.

"Some Muslim clerics—citing war verses from the Koran and the Hadith and reciting how Mohammed himself acted out such verses in Medina, Mecca and other sites—are guilty of inciting murder, rape and mayhem, all in the name of God.

"Nazism, exploiting modern weapons maximally, surpassed the evil perpetrated by prior marauders. Communism—

exploiting modern weaponry in concert with even more ruthless indoctrinations—has bested even Nazism's apex of evil to an even more widespread degree. So now also venally Koranic Islam, because it has spread worldwide, is currently capable of surpassing the evil wrought by Nazism and Communism combined.

"Millions of Muslims who live peaceably are caught in a tragic vise. Taught, often from childhood, that denying the divine inspiration of every word of the Koran is a capital crime, they eventually learn that those supposedly inspired words require them, for example, to 'wage war in the cause of Allah until Islam is the only religion.' To reject such commands as false subjects them to be judged by other Muslims as guilty of a capital crime. The moment they endorse such commands as validated by God, in that moment they become no longer trustworthy, though they may hope still to appear so among non-Muslim acquaintances.

AS FOR VIOLENCE DONE IN THE NAME OF CHRIST

"Until the time of Augustine of Hippo, Christians in the Roman Empire were renowned as people willing to *endure* persecution and even martyrdom while seeking to spare others from duress. That pristine ideal prevailed until Augustine subtly introduced a variant doctrine designed to weaken the Christian credo that the Church must always rely solely on *divine* charisma as opposed to harnessing the secular power of the Roman State.

"Until Augustine's day, Christians believed that God *draws* sinners to repentance and redemption via prevenient grace. Augustine, by adding a spin to certain biblical texts, insisted that mankind's natural state is so demented that people are incapable of responding to prevenient grace, hence prevenient grace must be replaced by *irresistible election*, meaning that every person's initial response to God has to be programmed robotically. If you recall my earlier comments, we as citizens created in Valcon's image are endowed with free will, whatever the consequence.

"A flaw lay hidden in Augustine's seemingly innocent change. Christians take God as their example. As surely as God irresistibly converts indisposed people, shouldn't a key Christian leader follow his example, perhaps even by subjoining the force of the Roman State to compel entire populations according to the will of the Church as defined by the key leader? Augustine began to see himself as helping God coerce the will of the Roman State so as to achieve the righteous will of God via a state-empowered Church.

"North African Christians led by a pastor named Donatus, sensing error in Augustine's innovation, separated from sectors of the Church that agreed with him. Augustine, well-connected with officials in Rome, asked *them* to pressure the Donatists on his behalf. The Roman State responded by 'irresistibly' persecuting Donatus and scattering his followers. Other Church Fathers came close to disbarring Augustine as a result, but in the end they chose (and some modern theologians *still* choose) to look the other way.

"Over time, Augustine's devious example inspired pope after pope to permit mobs of so-called Christians to persecute Jews. They also launched inquisitions against Christians who dismissed the pope-dominated version of the church as no longer 'the bride of Christ' on Earth. In their eyes, she had become instead an errant 'Queen' of political Rome. Eventually that church, via the secular state, abetted anti-Muslim crusades. John the Apostle prophesied of her:

> "In her heart she boasts, 'I sit enthroned as queen. I am not a widow [*in the sense of awaiting the return of her Husband from heaven*]; I will never mourn." [*Of course! By marrying her former persecutor, she has freed herself from persecution only to become a persecutor herself*]. [Revelation 18:7]

"Centuries later, John Calvin, Martin Luther *et al.*—though leading a movement against the church *a là* Augustine—sadly chose to add Augustine's irresistible election concept to what became a less-than-truly-reformed theology. Once again, belief that God, our prime example, coerces human compliance irresistibly, led these key leaders astray. Protestant Reformers paralleled Augustine's violence against Donatists by killing not only heretics but even Christians who avowed prevenient grace as God's choice in this age. Martin Luther, near the end of his life, encouraged Lutherans to persecute German Jews. His sermon, *The

Jews and Their Lies, exploited by later hatemongers including Adolf Hitler, was used to justify larger-scale anti-Jewish atrocities.

"I urge those who blame *all* Christians, including prevenient-grace believers, for blatant episodes of violence in the history of Christianity, to desist in the name of fairness. People victimized by that same category of violence should not be listed among its perpetrators."

Kent was shocked. Never in all his years of training had he heard anyone critique Augustine so categorically. Still, to his surprise, he found himself agreeing with Kaidan. As for Justine, she was intrigued by Kaidan's way of linking a subtle doctrinal shift with its psychologically induced aftermath.

AND THE END RESULT THIS TIME WILL BE...

"An earlier downward social spiral," Kaidan added, "led Valcon several millennia ago to destroy Earth's pre-Flood civilization, followed later by his destruction of Sodom and Gomorrah. Earth's present downward spiral is accelerating worldwide even at this moment. Judgment impends!

"This time, however, God's judgment of the wicked will be preceded by a very different rescue operation for the righteous. More than that, Earth's ensuing judgment will be followed by a glorious restoration of full 7th Harmony Ministration. What is now seen as 'a crucible planet where evil must be incarcerated until its ultimate metastasis' will then be a fully redeemed world.

"Christ, King of the cosmos, even now approaches this planet in his bodily form. It was here that he, God the Son, became incarnated also as 'the Son of man.' Rather than an ark, this time a planet-encircling fleet of starships from various worlds will rescue righteous people. Some of our spaceships are several miles in diameter with ample space to transport all whom we must take from Earth to a heaven that is central to this entire cosmos. As Jesus promised:

> "...he will send his angels [among whom I am a forerunner] and gather his elect from the four winds, from the ends of the earth... [Mark 13:27].

"And as his servant Paul affirmed:

"...the dead in Christ will rise first. After that, we who are
still alive and are left will be caught up together with them
in the clouds to meet the Lord in the air. And so we will be
with the Lord forever. [I Thessalonians 4:16, 17]

"I must now bid you all farewell," Kaidan said in a tone of
joy mingled with sorrow. "My mission is complete. I must return
to my starship and depart to join the approaching armada. Some of
us will meet again soon. Would that all of us could meet again, but
for that to happen, each person must choose to be reconciled to
Valcon. Adieu!" With that, Kaidan left the stage.

Within the hour, people at Central Park watched Kaidan
arrive by helicopter and wave to them as he entered his spaceship.
Minutes after he closed the door behind him, his craft arose
vertically and vanished beyond the clouds.

Two weeks later, Kent and Becky, watching the news at
home, noted differing categories of reaction to Kaidan's teaching.
Muslims, Hindus, many Buddhists, atheists and Communists
worldwide remained strongly opposed. Elsewhere, churches were
described as filled to overflow. Sans church buildings, people were
meeting in homes or out in the open to discuss Kaidan's teaching
and to worship God. Sales of Bibles had accelerated. Christian
media reported people helping each other trace links between the
Unified Field and passages in Scripture. Becky said, "James Engle
isn't the only person with a lot of catching up to do!"

By a third week other reports began surfacing. Even amid
the ranks of Communists, Muslims, Hindus and Buddhists, some
people were joyfully proclaiming themselves as followers of Jesus
Christ. Numerous politicians, some college professors and prison
inmates were expressing faith.

On the negative side, the man who had expertly translated
Kaidan's entire teaching into Arabic—Salim Kumer—had been
found murdered in his New York apartment the day before. The
Hindi translator in the next booth said an imam ordered Salim to
cease translating if Kaidan said anything positive about Judeo-

Christian belief. When such a moment came, Salim refused to stop translating, saying, "My fellow Arabs need to hear these things!"

The imam thought to have murdered or ordered the murder of Salim Kumer had already departed to Saudi Arabia. Kaidan's Symposium had recorded its first martyr.

Charles Stein announced that Kaidan's presentation of God as a Value Continuum who is corollary to the extent continuum had taken him by surprise and "leveraged him over to faith." He and his wife, Alicia, were happily reunited, worshipping together at the evangelical church where she had long been a member.

Communist nations, disbelieving everything Kaidan taught during his second day, had resolved to continue operations as usual. Muslim leaders from Tehran to Morocco were expressing confidence that Islam's Mahdi would arrive in time to counter what Judeo-Christianity's "accomplice" from Arkona had taught. ISIS and al-Qaida jihadists announced intentions to continue forcing millions of Muslim refugees to seek sanctuary in Europe and the West as a cloak for their own jihadist invasion.

Then came a news flash:

"NASA has sighted a swarm of enormously large space-ships approaching Earth from a region of space somewhere far below the South Pole. Is this an invasion or, as Arkona's very short-term ambassador to Earth recently implied, *a rescue op*?

"If in fact this is an invasion, Earth may be about to suffer an enormous blitzkrieg. If this is a rescue op, conceivably Earth's population could soon be doubly or perhaps even triply decimated! Stand by for further reports."

Notes

[1]Neil deGrasse Tyson and Donald Goldsmith, *Origins: Fourteen Billion Years of Cosmic Evolution*. New York: W. W. Norton & Company, Inc., ©2004 by Neil deGrasse Tyson and Donald Goldsmith, p. 127. Used by permission of W. W. Norton & Company, Inc., here and in subsequent references to this work. These selections may not be reproduced, stored in a retrieval system, or transmitted in any form or by any means without prior written permission of the publisher.

[2]*Ibid.*, p. 26.

[3]*Ibid.*

[4]*Ibid.*, p. 42.

[5]*Ibid.*, p. 28.

[6]*Ibid.*, p. 51.

[7]*Ibid.*

[8]*Ibid.*, p. 127.

[9]*Ibid.*, p. 150.

[10]*Ibid.*, pp. 71-72.

[11]Giles Sparrow, *Cosmos: A Field Guide*. London: Quercus, 2006, p. 215.

[12]Tyson and Goldsmith, *op. cit.*, pp. 51-52.

[13]*Ibid.*, p. 42.

[14]*Ibid.*,, p.51.

[15]Raman Prinja, *Visions of the Universe*. New York: Barnes and Noble Publishing, 2005, p. 90.

[16]Steve Nadis, "Dark Matter Deniers: Exploring a blasphemous alternative to one of modern physics' most vexing enigmas," *Discover* 36:6 (July/August 2015), pp. 40-43.

[17]Prinja, *op. cit.*, p. 64.

[18]*Ibid.*, p. 65.

[19]National Geographic Society, *The New Universe: Here, Now and Beyond*. Washington, DC, 2010, pp. 86-87.

[20]Tyson and Goldsmith, *op. cit.*, p. 74.

Glossary

Continuum: Something comprised of parts that cannot be separated nor even separately discerned.

Extent continuum: The invisible, infinitely solid union of length, width, height and time. The extent continuum is invisible because although we see objects and events occurring in it, we cannot see space-time itself. The extent continuum must also be deemed infinitely solid simply because even if it did consist of particles, the gaps between the particles would also have to be extent continuous with the particles. As an infinite solid, extent cannot be destroyed nor can it be torn, but it can be compressed or stretched provided inverse equality is conserved. And that is exactly how the Value Continuum (see below) creates matter and energy as inversely equal alterations within the otherwise homogeneous extent continuum. Degrees of alteration define mass. The direction of alteration defines charge. The inverse equality requirement is the basis of conservation laws.

Sub-extent continuum: The mutual melding of the four extent dimension yields four sub-extent continua: A, B. C and D. In A, **length** is basic with width, height and time added. In B, **width** is basic with length, height and time added. In C, **height** is basic with length, width and time added. In D, **time** is basic, with length, width and height added. Chapter 11 explains how **quarks** derive from these six different combinations of A, B, C and D.

Value Continuum: This is the equally invisible, eternal corollary of the extent continuum wherein three value dimensions—infinite intellect, i.e., **omniscience**; infinite emotion, i.e., **omnisentience** and infinite will, i.e., **omnipotence**—by their mutual inhering comprise three infinite Persensions (see the next Glossary item).

Persension: Just as the mutual melding of four extent dimensions yields four sub-extent continua, so also the mutual melding of three value dimensions yields three infinite Sub-Value Continua known as Persensions, This is a new word coined by fusing the word 'person' with the word 'dimension.' In one Persension, **omniscience** is basic with omnisentience and omnipotence added. In a second Persension, **omnisentience** is basic with omniscience and omnipotence added. In a third Persension, **omnipotence** is basic with omniscience and omnisentience added. Obviously each Sub-Value Continuum is thus an infinite Person yet all three together comprise one Person—God!

These are known on Earth as the three Persons of the Godhead: Father, Son and Holy Spirit. In Unified Field terms, they are called the Persension of Omniscience, the Persension of Omnisentience and the Persension of Omnipotence.

Made in the USA
Charleston, SC
10 March 2016